Rolling Stones Complete

Omnibus Press/EMI Music Publishing Ltd.

Distributed to the Music Trade by:
E.M.I. Music Publishing Limited,
138-140 Charing Cross Road, London WC2H 0LD
Music Sales Limited,
78 Newman Street, London W1P 3LA.

Distributed to the Book Trade by:
Book Sales Limited,
78 Newman Street, London W1P 3LA.

Book and cover design by Howard Brown

Thanks to Rex Features, London Features International
and Camera Press for photographs used
throughout this book.

Printed in England by
William Clowes (Beccles) Limited, Beccles and London.
Reproduction by
East Anglian Engraving Company Limited, Norwich.

Contents

Discography

A complete listing of all officially released
UK records from 1963 to 1982.

The Lyrics

Complete words to all the Stones songs. Lyrics
numbered 1 to 169 run in alphabetical sequence.
Lyrics 170 to 193 were late additions to the book and
consist of the infamous 'Cocksucker Blues' (never
officially released) plus words from the album
'Emotional Rescue'.

The Music

Arranged for easy guitar with chord symbols and
complete words. The music runs in the same order
and is numbered to match the lyrics section.

Index

An alphabetical listing of all songs.

Supplement

The Discographies to 'Tattoo You' and 'Still Life',
and The Lyrics and the Music to 'Tattoo You'
(Nos 181-193).

Discography

Come On (Berry)/**I Want To Be Loved** (Dixon)
Decca F11675. Released: June 7, 1963
Produced: Impact Sound

Poison Ivy (Leiber, Stoller)/**Fortune Teller** (Neville)
Decca F11742, Released: Cancelled
Produced: Impact Sound

Thank Your Lucky Stars Volume Two

Decca LK 4554. Released: September 1963
The Rolling Stones – Come On (Berry)
Other artists included:
The Bachelors – Faraway Places/The Big Three –
By The Way/ The Cadets – Hello Trouble/The
Caravelles – You Don't Have To Be A Baby To Cry/
Billie Davis – He's The One/The Dennisons – Be My
Girl/Karl Denver – Still/Lorne Gibson Trio – Some
Do, Some Don't/Jet Harris and Tony Meehan – Foot
Stomp/Heinz – Just Like Eddie/Kathy Kirby – Dance
On/The Marauders – That's What I Want/Mickie
Most – Mr Porter/Brian Poole – Twist And Shout/
The Tornadoes – Ice Cream Man

I Wanna Be Your Man (Lennon, McCartney)/**Stoned**
(Nanker, Phelge)
Decca F 11764. Released: November 1, 1963
Produced: Impact Sound

The Rolling Stones

Bye Bye Johnny (Berry)/Money (Gordy Jr,
Bradford)/You Better Move On (Alexander)/Poison
Ivy (Leiber, Stoller)
Decca DFE 8560. Released: January 17, 1964
Produced: Impact Sound

Ready, Steady, Go!

Decca LK 4577. Released: January 1964
The Rolling Stones – Come On (Berry)/I Wanna Be
Your Man (Lennon, McCartney)
Other artists included:
The Big Three – I'm With You/The Chucks – The
Hitch-Hiker/Bern Elliott – Money/Jet Harris and Tony
Meehan – Applejack/Heinz – Country Boy/Peter Jay
and The Jaywalkers – Kansas City/Kathy Kirby –
Secret Love/Peter Maclaine – Yes, I Do/The Mojos –
Forever/Brian Poole – Do You Love Me?/Brian
Poole – Twist And Shout/The Rockin' Berries –
Itty Bitty Pieces/The Tornadoes – Dragonfly

Saturday Club

Decca LK 4583. Released: January 1964
The Rolling Stones – Poison Ivy (Leiber,
Stoller)/Fortune Teller (Neville)
Other artists included:
Dave Berry – Memphis, Tennessee/The Chimes –
Say It Again/Karl Denver – I Forgot What It Was
Like/Lorne Gibson Trio – Go Easy With My Heart/
Jet Harris and Tony Meehan – Applejack/Ted Heath
Music – Saturday Club Theme/Kathy Kirby – Bye Bye
Birdie/Kathy Kirby – Dance On/The Marauders –
Greenback Dollar/Brian Poole – Do You Love Me?/
Brian Poole – Twenty Miles/Doug Sheldon – Mickey's

Monkey/The Tornadoes – Telstar/The Vernon Girls –
Do You Know What I Mean?

Not Fade Away (Petty, Hardin)/**Little By Little**
(Phelge, Spector)
Decca F 11845. Released: February 21, 1964
Produced: Impact Sound

The Rolling Stones

Decca LK 4605. Released: April 26, 1964
Produced: Andrew Loog Oldham and Eric Easton for
Impact Sound
Route 66 (Troup)/I Just Want To Make Love To You
(Dixon)/Honest I Do (Reed)/I Need You Baby
[Mona] (McDaniels)/Now I've Got A Witness [Like
Uncle Phil and Uncle Gene] (Phelge)/Little By Little
(Phelge, Spector)/I'm A King Bee (Moore)/Carol
(Berry)/Tell Me [You're Coming Back] (Jagger,
Richard)/Can I Get A Witness (Holland, Dozier,
Holland)/You Can Make It If You Try
(Jarrett)/Walking The Dog (Thomas)

Fourteen

Decca LK 4695. Released: May 21, 1964
The Rolling Stones – Surprise, Surprise (Jagger,
Richard)
Other artists included:
The Applejacks – Baby's In Black/The Bachelors –
Maureen/Dave Berry – He's With You/Bern Elliott –
Forget Her/Billy Fury – This Diamond Ring/The
Johnny Howard Band – Tomboy/Tom Jones – Kiss,
Kiss/Kathy Kirby – Soon I'll Wed My Love/Mike
Leander Orchestra – Sandstorm/Lulu and The Luvvers
– Just One Look/Them – Little Girl/Unit Four Plus
Two – Women From Liberia/The Zombies –
Nothing's Changed
NB Entire profits from this record together with
royalties from the artists were donated to The Lords
Taverners National Playing Fields Association.

It's All Over Now (B and S Womack)/**Good Times,
Bad Times** (Jagger, Richard)
Decca F 11934. Released: June 26, 1964
Produced: Impact Sound

Five By Five

If You Need Me (Pickett, Bateman, Sanders)/Empty
Heart (Nanker, Phelge)/2120 South Michigan Avenue
(Nanker, Phelge)/Confessin' The Blues (Brown,
McShann)/Around And Around (Berry)
Decca DFE 8590. Released: August 14, 1964
Arranged: The Rolling Stones
Produced: Andrew Loog Oldham for Impact Sound

Little Red Rooster (Dixon)/**Off The Hook**
(Nanker, Phelge)
Decca F 12014. Released: November 13, 1964
Produced: Impact Sound

The Rolling Stones No. 2

Decca LK 4661. Released: January 30, 1965
Produced: Andrew Loog Oldham for Impact Sound
Everybody Needs Somebody To Love (Russell, Burke,

Wexler)/Down Home Girl (Leiber, Butler)/You Can't Catch Me (Berry)/Time Is On My Side (Meade, Norman)/What A Shame (Jagger, Richard)/Grown Up Wrong (Jagger, Richard)/Down The Road Apiece (Raye)/Under The Boardwalk (Resnick, Young)/I Can't Be Satisfied (Waters)/Pain In My Heart (Neville)/Off The Hook (Jagger, Richard)/Susie Q (Hawkins, Lewis, Broadwater)

The Last Time (Jagger, Richard)/**Play With Fire** (Nanker, Phelge)
Decca F 12104. Released: February 26, 1965
Produced: Impact Sound

Got Live If You Want It!
We Want The Stones (Nanker, Phelge)Everybody Needs Somebody To Love (Russell, Burke, Wexler)/Pain In My Heart (Redding, Walden)/Route 66 (Troup)/I'm Moving On (Snow)/I'm Alright (Nanker, Phelge)
Decca DFE 8620. Released: June 11, 1965
Arranged: The Rolling Stones
Produced: Andrew Loog Oldham for Impact Sound

[I Can't Get No] Satisfaction (Jagger, Richard)/**The Spider And The Fly** (Nanker, Phelge)
Decca F 12220. Released: August 20, 1965
Produced: Andrew Loog Oldham

Out Of Our Heads
Decca SKL 4733. Released: September 6, 1965
Produced: Andrew Loog Oldham
She Said Yeah (Jackson, Christy)/Mercy, Mercy (Covay, Miller)/Hitch Hike (Gaye, Stevenson, Paul)/That's How Strong My Love Is (Jamison)/Good Times (Cooke)/Gotta Get Away (Jagger, Richard)/Talkin' 'Bout You (Berry)/Cry To Me (Russell)/Oh Baby [We Got A Good Thing Going] (Ozen)/Heart Of Stone (Jagger, Richard)/The Under Assistant West Coast Promotion Man (Nanker, Phelge)/I'm Free (Jagger, Richard)

Get Off Of My Cloud (Jagger, Richard)/**The Singer Not The Song** (Jagger, Richard)
Decca F 12263. Released: October 22, 1965
Produced: Andrew Loog Oldham

19th Nervous Breakdown (Jagger, Richard)/**As Tears Go By** (Jagger, Richard, Oldham)
Decca F12331. Released: February 4, 1966
Produced: Andrew Loog Oldham

Aftermath
Decca SKL 4786. Released: April 1966
Produced: Andrew Loog Oldham
Mother's Little Helper/Stupid Girl/Lady Jane/Under My Thumb/Doncha Bother Me/Goin' Home/Flight 505/High And Dry/Out Of Time/It's Not Easy/I Am Waiting/Take It Or Leave It/Think/What To Do
All compositions Jagger, Richard

Paint It Black (Jagger, Richard)/**Long Long While** (Jagger, Richard)
Decca F 12395. Released: May 13, 1966

Produced: Andrew Loog Oldham

Have You Seen Your Mother, Baby, Standing In The Shadow? (Jagger, Richard)/**Who's Driving Your Plane** (Jagger, Richard)
Decca F 12497. Released: September 23, 1966
Produced: Andrew Loog Oldham

Big Hits [High Tide And Green Grass]
Decca TXS 101. Released: November 1966
Produced: Andrew Loog Oldham
Have You Seen Your Mother, Baby, Standing In The Shadow? (Jagger, Richard)/Paint It Black (Jagger, Richard)/It's All Over Now (Womack)/The Last Time (Jagger, Richard)/Heart Of Stone (Jagger, Richard)/Not Fade Away (Petty, Hardin)/Come On (Berry)/[I Can't Get No] Satisfaction (Jagger, Richard)/Get Off Of My Cloud (Jagger, Richard)/As Tears Go By (Jagger, Richard, Oldham)/19th Nervous Breakdown (Jagger, Richard)/Lady Jane (Jagger, Richard)/Time Is On My Side (Meade, Norman)/Little Red Rooster (Dixon)

Let's Spend The Night Together (Jagger, Richard)/**Ruby Tuesday** (Jagger, Richard)
Decca F12546. Released: January 13, 1967
Produced: Andrew Loog Oldham

Between The Buttons
Decca SKL 4852. Released: January 20, 1967
Produced: Andrew Loog Oldham
Yesterday's Papers/My Obsession/Back Street Girl/Connection/She Smiled Sweetly/Cool, Calm And Collected/All Sold Out/Please Go Home/Who's Been Sleeping Here?/Complicated/Miss Amanda Jones/Something Happened To Me Yesterday
All compositions Jagger, Richard

We Love You (Jagger, Richard)/**Dandelion** (Jagger, Richard)
Decca F 12654. Released: August 18, 1967
Produced: Andrew Loog Oldham

Their Satanic Majesties Request
Decca TXS 103. Released: December 1967
Produced: The Rolling Stones
Sing This All Together/Citadel/In Another Land (Wyman)/2000 Man/Sing This All Together [See What Happens]/She's A Rainbow/The Lantern/Gomper/2000 Light Years From Home/On With The Show
All compositions Jagger, Richard except where indicated

Jumpin' Jack Flash (Jagger, Richard)/**Child Of The Moon** (Jagger, Richard)
Decca F 12782. Released: May 24, 1968
Produced: Jimmy Miller

Beggars Banquet
Decca SKL 4955. Released: December 5, 1968
Produced: Jimmy Miller

Sympathy For The Devil/No Expectations/Dear Doctor/Parachute Woman/Jig-Saw Puzzle/Street Fighting Man/Prodigal Son (Rev Robert Wilkins)/Stray Cat Blues/Factory Girl/Salt Of The Earth
All compositions Jagger, Richard except where indicated

Honky Tonk Women (Jagger, Richard)/**You Can't Always Get What You Want** (Jagger, Richard)
Decca F 12952. Released: July 11, 1969
Produced: Jimmy Miller
*Voices Arranged: Jack Nitzsche/Piano and Organ: Al Kooper

Through The Past, Darkly [Big Hits Volume 2]
Decca SKL 5019. Released: September 12, 1969
Produced: *Andrew Loog Oldham/**The Rolling Stones/***Jimmy Miller
Jumpin' Jack Flash/*Mother's Little Helper/**2000 Light Years From Home/*Let's Spend The Night Together/*You Better Move On (Alexander)/*We Love You/Street Fighting Man/**She's A Rainbow/*Ruby Tuesday/*Dandelion/*Sittin' On The Fence/***Honky Tonk Women
All compositions Jagger, Richard except where indicated

The Promotional Album
Decca RSM 1. Released: October 1969
Produced: *Andrew Loog Oldham/**The Rolling Stones/***Jimmy Miller
*Route 66 (Troup)/*Walking The Dog (Thomas)/*Around And Around (Berry)/*Everybody Needs Somebody To Love (Russell, Burke, Wexler)/*Off The Hook (Jagger, Richard)/*Suzie Q (Hawkins, Lewis, Broadwater)/*I'm Free (Jagger, Richard)/*She Said Yeah (Jackson, Christy)/*Under My Thumb (Jagger, Richard)/*Stupid Girl (Jagger, Richard)/**2000 Man (Jagger, Richard)/***Sympathy For The Devil (Jagger, Richard)/***Prodigal Son (Rev Robert Wilkins)/***Love In Vain (Payne)

Let It Bleed
Decca SKL 5025. Released: December 1969
Produced: Jimmy Miller
Gimmie Shelter/Love In Vain (Payne)/Country Honk/Live With Me/Let It Bleed/Midnight Rambler/You Got The Silver/Monkey Man/You Can't Always Get What You Want
All compositions Jagger, Richard except where indicated

Street Fighting Man (Jagger, Richard)/**Surprise, Surprise** (Jagger, Richard)
Decca F 13203. Released: July 20, 1970
Produced: *Jimmy Miller/**Andrew Loog Oldham

Get Yer Ya-Ya's Out!
Decca SKL 5065. Released: September 29, 1970
Produced: The Rolling Stones and Glyn Johns
Jumpin' Jack Flash/Carol (Berry)/Stray Cat

Blues/Love In Vain (Payne) (Trad Arr: Jagger, Richard)/Midnight Rambler/Sympathy For The Devil/Live With Me/Little Queenie (Berry)/Honky Tonk Women/Street Fighting Man
All compositions Jagger, Richard except where indicated

Cocksucker Blues (Jagger, Richard)
Decca: Unreleased
Produced: Mick Jagger

Brown Sugar (Jagger, Richard)/**Bitch** (Jagger, Richard)/***Let It Rock** (Anderson)
Rolling Stones RS 19100. Released: April 16, 1971
Produced: *Jimmy Miller/**Glyn Johns
Re-released in 208 Atlantic Gold Series January 12, 1974

Sticky Fingers
Rolling Stones COC 59100. Released: April 23, 1971
Produced: Jimmy Miller
Brown Sugar/Sway/Wild Horses/Can't You Hear Me Knocking/You Gotta Move (uncredited)/Bitch/I Got The Blues/Sister Morphine/Dead Flowers/Moonlight Mile
All compositions Jagger, Richard except where indicated

Stone Age
Decca SKL 5084. Released: April 23, 1971
Look What You've Done (Morganfield)/It's All Over Now (Womack)/Confessin' The Blues (Brown, McShann)/One More Try (Jagger, Richard)/As Tears Go By (Jagger, Richard, Oldham)/The Spider And The Fly (Nanker, Phelge)My Girl (Robinson, White)/Paint It Black (Jagger, Richard)/If You Need Me (Pickett, Bateman, Sanders)/The Last Time (Jagger, Richard)/Blue Turns To Grey (Jagger, Richard)/Around And Around (Berry)

Nicky Hopkins, Ry Cooder, Mick Jagger, Bill Wyman, Charlie Watts
Jamming With Edward
Rolling Stones COC 39100. Released: January 1972
Produced: Glyn Johns
The Boudoir Stomp (Hopkins, Cooder, Watts)/It Hurts Me Too (James)/Edwards Thrump Up (Hopkins, Cooder, Watts)/Blow With Ry (Hopkins, Cooder, Watts)/Interlude A La El Hopo (Hopkins, Cooder, Watts)/The Loveliest Night Of The Year (Webster, Ross)/Highland Fling (Hopkins, Cooder, Watts)

Milestones
Decca SKL 5098. Released: February 18, 1972
[I Can't Get No] Satisfaction/She's A Rainbow/Under My Thumb/I Just Want To Make Love To You (Dixon)/Yesterday's Papers/I Wanna Be Your Man (Lennon, McCartney)/Time Is On My Side (Meade, Norman)/Get Off Of My Cloud/Not Fade Away (Petty, Hardin)/Out Of Time/She Said Yeah (Jackson, Christy)/Stray Cat Blues

All compositions Jagger, Richard except where indicated

Tumbling Dice (Jagger, Richard)/**Sweet Black Angel** (Jagger, Richard)
Rolling Stones RS 19103. Released: April 14, 1972
Produced: Jimmy Miller

Exile On Main Street
Rolling Stones COC 69100. Released: May 12, 1972
Produced: Jimmy Miller
Rocks Off/Rip This Joint/Shake Your Hips (Moore)/Casino Boogie/Tumbling Dice/Sweet Virginia/Torn And Frayed/Sweet Black Angel/Loving Cup/Happy/Turd On The Run/Ventilator Blues (Jagger, Richard, Taylor)/I Just Want To See His Face/Let It Loose/All Down The Line/Stop Breaking Down (Trad Arr: Jagger, Richard, Wyman, Taylor, Watts)/Shine A Light/Soul Survivor
All compositions Jagger, Richard except where indicated

*Everybody Needs Somebody To Love (Russell, Burke, Wexler)/**Street Fighting Man (Jagger, Richard)/**Surprise Surprise** (Jagger, Richard)
Decca F 13195. Released: June 30, 1972
(33⅓ Maxi Single)
Produced: *Andrew Loog Oldham/**Jimmy Miller

Gimmie Shelter
Decca SKL 5101. Released: August 27, 1972
Jumpin' Jack Flash/Love In Vain/Honky Tonk Women/Street Fighting Man/Sympathy For The Devil/Gimmie Shelter/Under My Thumb/Time Is On My Side (Meade, Norman)/I've Been Loving You Too Long (Reading, Butler)/Fortune Teller (Neville)/Lady Jane/[I Can't Get No] Satisfaction
All compositions Jagger, Richard except where indicated

Rock 'N' Rolling Stones
Decca SKL 5149. Released: October 1972
Route 66 (Troup)/The Under Assistant West Coast Promotion Man (Nanker, Phelge)/Come On (Berry)/Talkin' 'Bout You (Berry)/Bye Bye Johnny (Berry)/Down The Road Apiece (Raye)/I Just Want To Make Love To You (Dixon)/Everybody Needs Somebody To Love (Russell, Burke, Wexler)/Oh, Baby [We Got A Good Thing Goin'] (Ozen)/19th Nervous Breakdown (Jagger, Richard)/Little Queenie (Berry)/Carol (Berry)

*Sad Day (Jagger, Richard)/**You Can't Always Get What You Want (Jagger, Richard)
Decca F 13404. Released: April 29, 1973
Produced: *Andrew Loog Oldham/**Jimmy Miller
Voices Arranged: **Jack Nitzsche
Piano and Organ: **Al Kooper

Angie (Jagger, Richard)/**Silver Train** (Jagger, Richard)
Rolling Stones RS 19105. Released: August 20, 1973
Produced: Jimmy Miller
Angie also released on:

By Invitation Only Atlantic K 60112 (1976)

Goats Head Soup
Rolling Stones COC 59101. Released: August 31, 1973
Produced: Jimmy Miller
Dancing With Mr D/100 Years Ago/Coming Down Again/Doo Doo Doo Doo Doo [Heartbreaker]/Angie/Silver Train/Hide Your Love/Winter/Can You Hear The Music/Star Star
All compositions Jagger, Richard

No Stone Unturned
Decca SKL 5173. Released: October 1973
Poison Ivy (Leiber, Stoller)/The Singer Not The Song (Jagger, Richard)/Surprise Surprise (Jagger, Richard)/Child Of The Moon (Jagger, Richard)/Stoned (Nanker, Phelge)/Sad Day (Jagger, Richard)/Money (Gordy, Jr, Bradford)/Congratulations (Jagger, Richard)/I'm Moving On (Snow)/2120 South Michigan Avenue (Nanker, Phelge)/Long Long While (Jagger, Richard)/Who's Driving Your Plane (Jagger, Richard)

*It's Only Rock 'N' Roll (Jagger, Richard)/**Through The Lonely Nights (Jagger, Richard)
Rolling Stones RS 19114. Released: July 26, 1974
Produced: *The Glimmer Twins/**The Glimmer Twins with Jimmy Miller
It's Only Rock 'N' Roll also released on:
By Invitation Only Atlantic K 60112 (1976)

It's Only Rock 'N' Roll
Rolling Stones COC 59103. Released: October 18, 1974. Produced: The Glimmer Twins
If You Can't Rock Me/Ain't Too Proud To Beg (Holland, Whitfield)/It's Only Rock 'N' Roll [But I Like It]/Till The Next Goodbye/Time Waits For No One/Luxury/Dance Little Sister/If You Really Want To Be My Friend/Short and Curlies/Fingerprint File
All compositions Jagger, Richard except where indicated

I Don't Know Why (Wonder, Riser, Hunter, Hardaway)/**Try A Little Harder** (Jagger, Richard)
Decca F 13584. Released: May 23, 1975

Made In The Shade
Rolling Stones COC 59104. Released: June 6, 1975
Produced: *Jimmy Miller/**The Glimmer Twins/
*Brown Sugar/*Tumbling Dice/*Happy/**Dance Little Sister/*Wild Horses/*Angie/*Bitch/**It's Only Rock 'N' Roll/*Doo Doo Doo Doo Doo [Heartbreaker]/*Rip This Joint
All compositions Jagger, Richard

Metamorphosis
Decca SKL 5212. Released: June 6, 1975
Produced: Andrew Loog Oldham, Jimmy Miller
Out Of Time/Don't Lie To Me (Berry)/Some Things Just Stick In Your Mind/Each And Everyday Of The Year/Heart Of Stone/I'd Much Rather Be With The Boys (Oldham, Richard)/[Walkin' Thru The] Sleepy City/We're Wasting Time/Try A Little Harder/I Don't Know Why (Wonder, Riser, Hunter, Hardaway)/If

You Let Me/Jiving Sister Fanny/Downtown Suzie (Wyman)/Family/Memo From Turner/I'm Going Down
All compositions Jagger, Richard except where indicated

Out Of Time (Jagger, Richard)/**Jiving Sister Fanny** (Jagger, Richard)
Decca F 13597. Released: September 5, 1975

Rolled Gold
[The Very Best Of The Rolling Stones)]
Decca ROST 1/2. Released: November 15, 1975
Come On/I Wanna Be Your Man/Not Fade Away/ Carol/It's All Over Now/Little Red Rooster/Time Is On My Side/The Last Time/[I Can't Get No] Satisfaction/Get Off Of My Cloud/19th Nervous Breakdown/As Tears Go By/Under My Thumb/Lady Jane/Out Of Time/Paint It Black/Have You Seen Your Mother, Baby, Standing In The Shadow?/Let's Spend The Night Together/Ruby Tuesday/Yesterday's Papers/We Love You/She's A Rainbow/Jumpin' Jack Flash/Honky Tonk Women/Sympathy For The Devil/Street Fighting Man/Midnight Rambler/ Gimmie Shelter

Honky Tonk Women (Jagger, Richard)/**Sympathy For The Devil** (Jagger, Richard)
Decca F 13635. Released: April 15, 1976
Produced: Jimmy Miller

Black And Blue
Rolling Stones COC 59106. Released: April 20, 1976
Produced: The Glimmer Twins
*Hot Stuff/**Hand Of Fate/***Cherry Oh Baby (Donaldson)/****Memory Motel/***Hey, Negrita/ Melody/**Fool To Cry/Crazy Mama
All compositions Jagger, Richard except where indicated
Featured guitarists include:
*Harvey Mandel/**Wayne Perkins/***Ronnie Wood/ ****Wayne Perkins and Harvey Mandel

Fool To Cry (Jagger, Richard)/**Crazy Mama** (Jagger, Richard)
Rolling Stones Records RS 19121. Released: April 20, 1976
Produced: The Glimmer Twins

Love You Live (Double Album)
Rolling Stones Records COC 89101. Released: September 1977
Produced: The Glimmer Twins
[Introduction] Excerpt from Fanfare For The Common Man by Aaron Copeland/Honky Tonk Women/If You Can't Rock Me/Get Off Of My Cloud/Happy/Hot Stuff/Star Star/Tumbling Dice/Fingerprint File/You Gotta Move (McDowell, Davis)/You Can't Always Get What You Want/Mannish Boy (London, McDaniel, Morganfield)/Crackin' Up/Little Red Rooster (Dixon)/Around And Around (Berry)/It's Only Rock 'N' Roll/Brown Sugar/Jumpin' Jack Flash/ Sympathy For The Devil
All compositions Jagger, Richard except where indicated

Featured artists include Billy Preston, Ian Stewart and Ollie Brown

Time Waits For No One: Anthology 1971-1977 (Compilation)
Rolling Stones Records COC 59107. Released: May 1979
Produced: The Glimmer Twins and Jimmy Miller
Time Waits For No One/Bitch/All Down The Line/ Dancing With Mr. D/Angie/Star Star/If You Can't Rock Me/Get Off Of My Cloud/Hand Of Fate/Crazy Mama/Fool To Cry

Some Girls
Rolling Stones Records CUN 39108. Released: June 9, 1978
Produced: The Glimmer Twins
Miss You/When The Whip Comes Down/Imagination (Whitfield, Strong)/Some Girls/Lies/Faraway Eyes/ Respectable/Before They Make Me Run/Beast Of Burden/Shattered
All compositions Jagger, Richard except where indicated
Featured guitarists include Ian 'Mac' McLagan

Respectable (Jagger, Richard)/**When The Whip Comes Down** (Jagger, Richard)
EMI 2861. Released: September 15, 1978
Produced: The Glimmer Twins

Miss You (Jagger, Richard)/**Girl With The Faraway Eyes** (Jagger, Richard)
EMI 2808. Released: May 19, 1978
12″ version released June 2, 1978 as 12EMI 2808.
Produced: The Glimmer Twins

Emotional Rescue (Jagger, Richards)/**Down In The Hole** (Jagger, Richards)
Rolling Stones Records RSR 105.
Released June 20, 1980
Produced: The Glimmer Twins

Emotional Rescue
Rolling Stones Records CUN 39111.
Released June 22, 1980
Produced: The Glimmer Twins.
Associate Producer: Chris Kimsey.
Dance (Jagger, Richards, Wood)/Summer Romance (Jagger, Richards)/Send It To Me (Jagger, Richards)/Let Me Go (Jagger, Richards)/Indian Girl (Jagger, Richards)/Where The Boys Go (Jagger, Richards)/Down The Hole (Jagger, Richards)/ Emotional Rescue (Jagger, Richards)/She's So Cold (Jagger, Richards)/All About You (Jagger, Richards)

The Lyrics

1
All Down The Line

Yeah, heard the diesel drumming all down the line
Oh, heard the wires a-humming all down the line
Yeah, hear the women sighing all down the line
Oh, hear the children crying all down the line

(All down the line)
We'll be watching out for trouble, yeah
(All down the line)
And we'd better keep the motor running, yeah
(All down the line)

Well, you can't say yes and you can't say no
Just be right there when the whistle blows
I need a sanctified girl
With a sanctified mind – to help me now

Yeah, all the people singing all down the line
Mmmm, watch the men all working, working, yeah
(All down the line)

(All down the line)
We're gonna open up the throttle, yeah
(All down the line)
We're gonna bust another bottle, yeah
(All down the line)
I need a shot of salvation, baby
Once in a while
Hear the whistle blowing
Hear it for ten thousand miles

(All down the line)
We're gonna open up the throttle, yeah
All down the line
We're gonna bust another bottle, yeah
Well, you can't say yes and you can't say no

Just be right there when the whistle blows
I need a sanctified mind to help me out right now

Be my little baby for a while
Won't you be my little baby for a while

2
All Sold Out

Why put this sadness inside of me
Why be so matter of fact
Why put this one bit of hope in me
You sold me out and that's that

I hope that you're having fun with me
There's not much left to attack
I hope that you're nearly done with me
You sold me out and that's that
All sold out
I felt so green
It was just like that
I was put down flat
I was sold out just like that

All sold out
I've never seen a mind so tangled
A girl so strangled
All sold out
I felt so green
It was just like that
I was put down flat
I was sold out just like that

I missed the point of you doing it
Your mind must've just jumped the tracks
I took a bit diff'rent view of it
You sold me out and that's that

4

As Tears Go By

Angie, oh, Angie, when will those dark clouds disappear
Angie, Angie, where will it lead us from here
With no loving in our souls and no money in our coats
You can't say we're satisfied
But Angie, Angie, you can't say we never tried

Angie, you're beautiful, but ain't it time we said goodbye
Angie, I still love you, remember all those nights we cried
All the dreams we held so close seemed to all go up in smoke
Let me whisper in your ear
Angie, Angie, where will it lead us from here

Oh, Angie, don't you weep, all your kisses still taste sweet
I hate that sadness in your eyes
But Angie, Angie, ain't time we said goodbye

With no loving in our souls and no money in our coats
You can't say we're satisfied
But Angie, I still love you, baby, ev'rywhere I look I see your eyes
There ain't a woman that comes close to you, come on, baby, dry your eyes

But Angie, Angie, ain't it good to be alive
Angie, Angie, they can't say we never tried

It is the evening of the day
I sit and watch the children play
Smiling faces I can see
But not for me
I sit and watch
As tears go by

My riches can't buy ev'rything
I want to hear the children sing
All I hear is the sound
Of rain falling on the ground
I sit and watch
As tears go by

It is the evening of the day
I sit and watch the children play
Doin' things I used to do
They think are new
I sit and watch
As tears go by

5

Back Street Girl

I don't want you to be high
I don't want you to be down
Don't want to tell you no lies
Just want you to be around
Please come right up to my ears
You will be able to hear what I say
Don't want you part of my world
Just you be my back street girl

Please don't be part of my life
Please keep yourself to yourself
Please don't you bother my wife
That way you won't get no help
Don't try to ride on my horse
You're rather common and coarse anyway
Don't want you part of my world
Just you be my back street girl

Please don't you call me at home
Please don't come knocking at night
Please never ring on the phone
Your manners are never quite right
Please take the favours I grant
Curtsy and look nonchalant just for me
Don't want you part of my world
Just you be my back street girl
Just you be my back street girl

6

Beast Of Burden

I'll never be your beast of burden
My back is broad but it's a hurting
All I want is for you to make love to me
I'll never be your beast of burden
I've walked for miles, my feet are hurting
All I want is for you to make love to me

Am I hard enough
Am I rough enough
Am I rich enough
I'm not too blind to see

I'll never be your beast of burden
So let's go home and draw the curtains
Music on the radio
Come on baby, make sweet love to me.

Am I hard enough
Am I rough enough
Am I rich enough
I'm not too blind to see – oh little sister
Pretty, pretty, pretty, pretty girl
You're such a pretty, pretty, pretty, pretty, pretty,
    pretty, girl
Pretty, pretty such a pretty, pretty, pretty girl.
Come on, baby please, please, please.

I'll tell ya –
You can put me out on the street
Put me out with no shoes on my feet
But put me out, put me out, put me out – out of
    misery
All your sickness I can suck it up
Throw it all at me
I can shrug it off
There's one thing, baby, I don't understand
You keep telling me I ain't your kind of man

Ain't I rough enough
Ain't I tough enough
Ain't I rich enough
In love enough
Oooo, ooh please.

I'll never be your beast of burden
I'll never be your beast of burden
Never, never, never, never, never, never, never be.
Never be your beast of burden
I've walked for miles and my feet are hurting
All I want is you to make love to me.

I don't need no beast of burden
I need no fussing, I need no nursing
Never, never, never, never, never, never, never be . . .

7
Before They Make Me Run

Worked the bars and side-shows,
Along the Twilight Zone,
Only a crowd can make you feel so alone,
And it really hit home.
Booze and pills and powders,
You have to choose your medicine,
Well, it's another good-bye,
To another good friend.

Well after all is said and done,
Gotta move, while it's still fun,
But let me walk, before they make me run.
After all is said and done,
I gotta move, it's still fun.
I'm gonna walk before they make me run.

Watch my tail-lights fading,
There ain't a dry eye in the house,
They're laughin' and singin', well they're dancin'
And drinkin' as I left town.
I'm gonna find my way to Heaven,
'Cause I did my time in Hell
I wasn't looking too good, but I was feeling real well.

Well after all is said and done,
I gotta move – I had my fun.
Let us walk, before they make us run.

Well after all is said and done,
I did alright an' had my fun.
But I will walk before they make me run
But I will walk before they make me run
But I will walk before they make me run
But I will walk before they make me run.

Well if it's all been said and done,
I gotta move, I had my fun,
But let me walk before they make me run
So let me walk before they make me run
I wanna walk before they make me run.

8
Bitch

I'm feeling so tired, can't understand it.
Just had a fortnight's sleep
I'm feeling so stoned, oooh so distracted
Ain't touched a thing all week

Feeling drunk, juiced up and sloppy
Ain't touched a drink all night
Feeling hungry, can't see the reason
Just had a horse meat pie

Yeah, when you call my name
I salivate like a Pavlov dog
Yeah, when you lay me out
My heart is beating louder than a big bass drum

You got to mix it, ya got to fix it child
It must be love, it's a bitch

You got to mix it, ya got to fix it child
It must be love, it's a bitch

Sometimes I'm sexy, more like a stud
Kicking the stall all night
Sometimes I'm so shy, got to be worked on
Don't have no bark or bite

Yeah, when you call my name
Salivate like a Pavlov dog
Yeah, when you lay me out
My heart is beating louder than a big bass drum

9
Blue Turns To Grey

Well, now that she is gone
You won't feel bad for long
For maybe just an hour
Or just a moment of the day
Then blue turns to grey
And try as you may
You just don't feel good
And you don't feel all right
And you know that you must
Find her find her find her

You think you'll have a ball
And you won't hurt at all
You'll find another girl
Or maybe more to pass the time away
Then blue turns to grey
And try as you may
You just don't feel good
And you don't feel all right
And you know that you must
Find her find her find her

She's not at home when you call
So then you go to all
All the places where she likes to be
But she has gone away
Then blue turns to grey
And try as you may
You just don't feel good
And you don't feel all right
And you know that you must
Find her find her find her

Blue turns to grey
Blue turns to grey

10
Brown Sugar

Gold Coast slave ship
Bound for cotton fields,
Sold in a market
Down in New Orleans
Scarred old slaver know
He's doing alright
Hear him whip the women
Just around midnight

Brown sugar, how come you taste so good?
Brown sugar, just like a young girl should

Drums beating
Cold English blood runs hot,
Lady of the house wondrin'
Where it's gonna stop
Houseboy knows
That he's doing alright
You should have heard him
Just around midnight

Brown sugar, how come you taste so good?
Brown sugar, just like a black girl should.

Brown sugar sho' tastes good
Brown sugar sho' tastes good
Brown sugar, how come you taste so good.

I bet your mama was
A tent show queen
And all her girl friends
Were sweet sixteen
I'm no schoolboy,
But I know what I like
You should have heard me
Just around midnight.

Brown sugar how come you taste so good
Brown sugar, just like a young girl should

11
Can You Hear The Music

Can you hear the music
Can you hear the music,
Can you hear the magic in the air
Can you feel the magic, oh yeah

Love is a mystery I can't demystify, oh no
And sometimes I wonder why we're here
But I don't care, no, I don't care

When I hear the drummer get me in the groove
When I hear the guitar makes you wanna move
Can you feel the magic floating in the air
Can you feel the magic, oh yeah

Sometimes you're feeling you've been pushed around
And your rainbow just ain't here
Don't you fear, don't you fear

When I hear the music, trouble disappears
When you hear the music ringing in your ears
Can you feel the magic floating in the air
Can you hear the magic, oh yeah

Love is a mystery, I can't demystify, oh no
Sometimes I'm dancing on air
But I get scared, I get scared

When you hear the music, ringing in the air
Can you hear the music, oh yeah
Can you hear the drummer makes me gotta groove

Can you hear the guitar makes me wanna move
Can you hear the music, oh yeah
Can you hear the music, right in my ear
Can you hear the music

12
Can't You Hear Me Knocking

Yeah, you've got satin shoes
Yeah, you've got plastic boots
Y'all got cocaine eyes
Yeah you got speed freak jive

Can't you hear me knocking on your window
Can't you hear me knocking on your door
Can't you hear me knocking down the dirty street

Help me baby, I ain't no stranger
Help me baby, I ain't no stranger
Help me baby, I ain't no stranger

Can't you hear me knocking when you're safe asleep
Can't you hear me knocking down the gas light street
Can't you hear me knocking throw me down the keys

All right now

Hear me ringing big bells toll
Hear me singing soft and low

I've been begging on my knees
I've been kicking help me please
Hear me prowling I'm gonna take you down
Hear me growling yeah I've got flat feet
Hear me howling I'm all around your street now
Hear me knocking I'm around your town

13

Casino Boogie

No good can't speak
Wound up no sleep
Sky diver inside her
Skip rope stunt flyer
Wounded lover
Got no time on hand

One last cycle
Thrill freak Uncle Sam
Pause for business hope you understand
Judge and jury walk out hand in hand
Dietrich movies close up boogies
Kissing cut in cans
Grotesque music million dollar sad
Go to tactics got no time on hand

Left shoe shuffle
Right shoe muffle
Sinking in the sand
Fade out freedom
Steaming heat on
Watch that hat in black
Finger twitching
Got no time on hand

14

Child Of The Moon

The wind blows rain into my face
The sun glows at the end of the highway
Child of the moon rub your rainy eyes
Child of the moon
Give me a wide-awake, crescent-shaped smile

She shivers, by the light she is hidden
She flickers, like a lamp lady vision
Child of the moon rub your rainy eyes
Child of the moon
Give me a wide-awake, crescent-shaped smile

The first car on the foggy road riding
The last star for my lady is pining
Child of the moon bid the sun arise
Child of the moon
Give me a misty day, pearly grey
Silver silky faced, wide-awake, crescent-shaped
    smile

15

Citadel

Men at arms shout, 'Who goes there?'
We have journeyed far from here
Armed with bibles make us swear

Candy and Cathy, hope you both are well
Please come and see me in the citadel

Flags are flying dollar bills
From the heights of concrete hills
You can't see the pinnacles

Candy and Cathy, hope you both are well
Please come and see me in the citadel

In the streets of many walls
Here the peasants come and crawl
You can hear their numbers called

Candy and Cathy, hope you both are well
Please come and see me in the citadel

Screaming people fly so fast
In their shiny metal cars
Through the woods of steel and glass

Candy and Cathy, hope you both are well
Please come and see me in the citadel

16

Coming Down Again

Coming down again, coming down again
Coming down again, coming down again

Share your thoughts, there's nothing you can hide
She was dying to survive
I was caught, oh, taken for a ride
She was showing no surprise

Coming down again, coming down again
Where are all my friends, coming down again
Coming down again, coming down again
On the ground again, coming down again

Slipped my tongue in someone else's pie
Tasting better ev'ry time
She turned green and tried to make me cry
Being hungry ain't no crime

Coming down again, coming down again
Where are all my friends, coming down again
Coming down again, coming down again
On the ground again, coming down again

Coming down again, coming down again
Coming down again, coming down again

17
Complicated

She looks so simple in her way
She does the same thing ev'ry day
But she's dedicated to having her own way
She's very complicated

Women seem to fill her mind
And many men in so short time
But she's underrated. She treats me oh so kind
She's very complicated

We talk together and discuss
What is really best for us
She's sophisticated. My head's fit to bust
Cause she's so complicated

She knows just how to please her man
She's softer than a baby lamb
But she's very educated and doesn't give a damn
She's very complicated

18
Congratulations

Congratulations, congratulations

Well done, my friend
You've done it again
You've gone and broke another heart
Yeah tore it apart

You've done it before
Hope do it some more
You've got it down to a fine art

Remember the first time
You made a fool out of me
There'll be no next time
Just wait and see

Congratulations, congratulations
You've gone and broke another heart
Yeah tore it apart

19

Connection

All I want to do is get back to you
Connection I just can't make no connection
But all I want to do is to get back to you

Ev'rything is going in the wrong direction
The doctor wants to give me more injections
Giving me shots for a thousand rare infections
And I don't know if he'll let me go

Connection I just can't make no connection
But all I want to do is to get back to you
Connection I just can't make no connection
But all I want to do is get back to you

My bags they get a very close inspection
I wonder why it is that they suspect on
They're dying to add me to their collection
And I don't know if they'll let me go

Connection I just can't make no connection
But all I want to do is to get back to you
Connection I just can't make no connection
But all I want to do is to get back to you

20

Cool, Calm And Collected

Well, she's very wealthy it's true
So in that she is one up on you
She's dressed all in red white and blue
And she always knows more than you do
She's so affected
Cool calm collected

She knows who to smile to today
She has just been brought up in that way
She knows all the right games to play
And she always just knows what to say
She's well respected
Cool calm collected

In public the strain's hard to bear
But she exudes such a confident air
But behind she is not without care
But she sweeps it right under her hair
She's well respected
Cool calm collected

She seems to glow brilliantly white
And her hair seems to shine in the night
With her feet unbelievably light
And her teeth ready sharpened to bite
She's so respected
Cool calm collected

21
Country Honk

I'm sittin' in a bar, tippling a jar in Jackson
And on the street the summer sun it shines
There's many a barroom queen I've had in Jackson
But I just can't seem to drink you off my mind
It's those honky tonk women
Gimme, gimme, gimme the honky tonk blues

I laid a divorcee in New York City
I had to put up some kind of a fight
The lady she all dressed me up in roses
She blew my nose and then she blew my mind
It's those honky tonk women
Gimme, gimme, gimme the honky tonk blues

It's those honky tonk women
Gimme, gimme, gimme the honky tonk blues

22
Crazy Mama

Well you're crazy, mama
With your ball and chain
And your sawn off shotgun
And your blown out brains
Yes
You can scandalize me
Scorn my name
And you can steal my money
And that don't mean a doggone thing
Cause if you really think you can push it
I'm gonna bust your knees with a bullet
You're crazy, mama ah yeh

Well your old time religion
Is just a superstition
You're gonna pay high prices
For your sacrifices ah yeh

All your blood and thunder
Sure can't faze me none
If you gonna keep on coming
I'm gonna take it all head on
And if you don't believe I'm gonna do it
Just wait till you get hit by that bullet
You're crazy, mother I'm coming down to get you
now

Don't think I ain't thought about it
But it sure makes my shackles rise
And cold blood murder
It makes me want to draw the line

Well you're crazy, mother
With your ball and chain
You're plain psychotic
Plain insane
If you don't believe I'm gonna do it
Just wait for the thud of the bullet
You're crazy, mother yes
You crazy mothers yes
You crazy mothers yes
Crazy mothers

23
Dance Little Sister

On Thursday night she looked a fright
Her picki hair all curled, oh Lord what a sight
Dance dance little sister dance
On Friday night she's all decked out
Her high heeled shoes her dress so tight
Dance, dance little sister dance
On Saturday night she bassadee
She stepping high on Fred'rick Street
Dance, dance little sister dance

I said dance dance little sister dance
Dance little sister dance little sister dance
I said dance dance little sister dance
Dance little sister dance dance little sister dance

It make me hot
I'm wet with sweat
It burn like hell
I've four hours left
Dance, dance little sister dance

Get next to me drive me close
Don't mammaguay me
I lose control
Dance, dance little sister dance

I said dance dance little sister dance
Dance little sister dance dance little sister dance
I said dance dance little sister dance
Dance little sister dance dance little sister dance

Jump out of Africa
With a step that looks so bold
Ah when ya kickin' high
It make me blood run cold

I said dance dance little sister dance
Dance little sister dance dance little sister dance
I said dance dance little sister dance
Dance little sister dance dance little sister dance
On Saturday night we don't go home we bacchanak
    there ain't no dawn
Dance little sister dance

I said dance dance little sister dance
Dance little sister dance dance little sister dance
I said dance dance little sister dance
Dance little sister dance dance little sister dance

24
Dancing With Mr. D

Down in the grave yard where we have our tryst
The air smells sweet, the air smells thick
He never smiles, his mouth merely twists
The breath in my lungs feels clinging and thick
Now I know his name, he's called Mr. D
And one of these days he's gonna set you free
Human skulls is hanging right round his neck
The palms of my hands feel clammy and wet

I was dancing, dancing, dancing so free
I was dancing, dancing, dancing so free
Dancing Lord take your hands off me
Dancing with Mister D, with Mister D, with
    Mister D

Will it be poison in my glass
Will it be slow or will it be fast
The bite of a snake the sting of a spider
A drink of belladonna of a Toussaint night
Hiding round a corner in New York city
Looking down a 44 in West Virginia
I was dancing, dancing, dancing so free
I was dancing, dancing, dancing so free
Dancing with Mister D

Mister D, Mister D, Mister D, Mister D
Dancing, dancing, dancing, dancing
Dancing, dancing, dancing, dancing

Dancing, dancing, dancing so free
I was dancing, dancing, dancing so free
Dancing Lord take your hands off me
Dancing with Mister D, Mister D, Mister D

One night I was dancing with a lady in black
Wearing black silk gloves and a black silk hat
She looked at me longing with black velvet eyes
She gazed at me strange all cunning and wise
Then I saw the flesh just fall off her bones
The eyes in her skull were just burning like coals
Lord have mercy fire and brimstone
I was dancing with Mister D

Dancing, dancing, dancing so free
I was dancing, dancing, dancing so free
Dancing Lord take your hands off me
Dancing with Mister D

25

Dandelion

Prince or pauper, beggar man or thief
Play the game with ev'ry blow you breathe
Dandelion don't tell no lies
Dandelion will make you wise
Tell me if she laughs or cries
Blow 'way dandelion

One o'clock, two o'clock, three o'clock, four o'clock,
    five o'clock
Dandelions don't care about the time
Dandelion don't tell no lies
Dandelion will make you wise
Tell me if she laughs or cries
Blow 'way dandelion
Blow 'way dandelion

So you're older now. Just the same
You can play the dandelion game
When you've finished with your childlike prayers
Well you know you should wear it

Tinker, tailor, soldier, sailor's life
Rich man, poor man, beautiful doctor's wife
Dandelion don't tell no lies
Dandelion will make you wise
Tell me if she laughs or cries
Blow 'way dandelion
Blow 'way dandelion

Little girls and boys come out to play
Bring your dandelions to blow away
Dandelion don't tell no lies
Dandelion will make you wise
Tell me if she laughs or cries
Blow 'way dandelion
Blow 'way dandelion

26

Dead Flowers

Well, when you're sitting there
In your silk upholstered chair
Talking to some rich folks that you know
Well I hope you won't see me
In my ragged company
You know I could never be alone

Take me down little Susie, take me down
I know you think you're the Queen of the
    Underground
And you can send me dead flowers every morning
Send me dead flowers by the mail
Send me dead flowers to my wedding
And I won't forget to put roses on your grave

Well, when you're sitting back
In your rose pink cadillac
Making bets on Kentucky Derby Day.
I'll be in my basement room
With a needle and a spoon
And another girl can take my pain away

Take me down little Susie, take me down
I know you think you're the Queen of the
    Underground
And you can send me dead flowers every morning
Send me dead flowers by the mail
Send me dead flowers to my wedding
And I won't forget to put roses on your grave

Take me down little Susie, take me down
I know you think you're the Queen of the
    Underground
And you can send me dead flowers every morning
Send me dead flowers by the US mail
Say it with dead flowers at my wedding
And I won't forget to put roses on your grave
No I won't forget to put roses on your grave

27
Dear Doctor

Oh help me, dear Doctor, I'm damaged
There's a pain where there once was a heart
It's sleeping, it's beating
Can't you please take it out
And preserve it right there in that jar

Oh help me, please mama, I'm sick'ning
It's to-day that's the day of the plunge
Oh the gal I'm to marry
Is a bow-legged sow
I've been soaking up drink like a sponge

'Don't you worry, get dressed', cried my mother
As she plied me with Bourbon so sour
'Pull your socks up, put your suit on
Comb your long hair down
For you will be wed in the hour'

Oh help me, dear Doctor, I'm damaged
There's a pain where there once was a heart
It's sleeping, it's beating
Can't you please take it out
And preserve it right there in that jar

I was trembling as I put on my jacket
It had creases as sharp as a knife
I put the ring in my pocket
But there was a note
And my heart it jumped into my mouth

It read, 'Darling I'm sorry to hurt you
But I've no courage to speak to your face
But I'm down in Virginia
With your cousin Lou
And there'll be no wedding to-day'

Oh help me, dear Doctor, I'm damaged
You can put back my heart in it's hole
Oh mama I'm crying
Tears of relief
And my pulse is now under control

28
Don'cha Bother Me

I said oh no don'tcha follow me no more
I said oh no don'tcha follow me no more
Well I am looking for my face
And I've got no place to go

I said oh no don'tcha follow me no more
I said oh no don'tcha follow me no more
Well pick your own mind
And don't touch mine no more

I'm still waiting here for a single idea
In your clothes and your hair
I wore it last year
Oh no don't you follow me no more

I said oh no don'tcha copy me no more
I said oh no don'tcha copy me no more
Well the lines around my eyes
Are protected by a copyright law

Well all the clubs and the bars and the little red cars
Not knowing why but trying to get high
Oh no don't you follow me no more
Don't you follow, don't you follow

29

Don't Lie To Me

Well let's talk it over babe before we start
I heard about the way you do your part
Don't lie to me don't you lie to me
Don't you make me mad I'll get evil as a man can be

Well of all kinds of people that I just can't stand
That's a lying woman and a cheating man
Don't lie to me don't you lie to me
Don't you make me mad I'll get evil as a man can be

Well I will love you baby and it ain't no lie
For every winter till the well runs dry
Don't lie to me don't you lie to me
Don't you make me mad I'm as shook up as a man
    can be

Well let's talk it over babe before we start
I heard about the way you do your part
Don't lie to me don't you lie to me
Don't you make me mad I'm as shook up as a man
    can be

Well let's talk it over babe before we start
I heard about the way you do your part
Don't lie to me don't you lie to me
Don't you make me mad I'll get evil as a man can be

30

Doo Doo Doo Doo Doo (Heartbreaker)

The police in New York City chased a boy right
    through the park
And in a case of mistaken identity they put a bullet
    through his heart
Heartbreaker with your forty-four, I wanna tear your
    world apart
Heartbreaker with your forty-four, I wanna tear your
    world apart

A ten year old girl on a street corner sticking needles
    in her arm
She died in the dirt of the alley way
Her mother said she had no chance, no chance
Heartbreaker, heartbreaker, she stuck the pins right
    in her heart
Heartbreaker, painmaker, you stole the love right out
    of my heart

Heartbreaker, heartbreaker, you stole the love right
    out of my heart
Heartbreaker, heartbreaker, I wanna tear the world
    apart

Doo doo doo doo do do doo . . .

31
Downtown Suzie

Got the Monday mornin' feel
Yeah, yeah, yeah
Monday wasn't really real
Yeah, yeah, Oh, yeah
Lying on a naked bed
Yeah, yeah, yeah
With an Alka Seltzer head
Yeah, yeah
Oh, Lucy looked sweet just a-strollin' down
   Newport Street
Talkin' 'bout Lu what ya gon' do?
I feel so bad
Have you ever been had?
I'll dry out sweet Lucy
Took an early morning shower
Yeah, yeah, yeah
Well, I wasted 'bout half an hour
Yeah, yeah ooh
I heard the ringing of the bell
Yeah, yeah, yeah
It's Lucy with the cleaning towel
Yeah, yeah
Oh, I'm feelin' like the Sunday Times
Yeah, yeah, yeah
A Southern Californian wine
Yeah, yeah
Lucy kicked me in the hole
Yeah, yeah, yeah
Tennis worth of achin' bones
Ooh-ooh
Oh Lucy looked sweet just a-strollin' down Newport
   Street
Talkin' 'bout Lu what ya gon' do?
I feel so bad
Have you ever been had?
I'll dry out sweet Lucy

32
Each And Every Day
Of The Year

Do I miss her just at night time
Arms around me till the right time
Yes I do,yes I do, yes I do, yes I do
Each and ev'ry day of the year

I still see her on the corner
Do I stop and still wait for her
Yes I do, yes I do, yes I do, yes I do
Each and ev'ry day of the year

Never get around any more
Don't know what my friends are for
No fun sitting all alone
When I cry cry cry on my own

Now that she is gone for ever
Do I wonder what my life's for
Yes I do, yes I do, yes I do, yes I do
Each and ev'ry day of the year

33

Empty Heart

An empty heart is like an empty life
I said an empty heart is like an empty life
It makes you feel like you wanna cry
Like you wanna cry like you wanna cry

Well you bin my lover for a long long time
Well you bin my lover for a long long time
'Cause you lived all alone in my town
I want my love again
I want my love again
I want my love again
I want it back again
I want it back again

34

Factory Girl

Waiting for a girl who's got curlers in her hair
Waiting for a girl who's got no money anywhere
We get buses ev'rywhere
Waiting for a factory girl

Waiting for a girl and her knees are much too fat
Waiting for a girl who wears scarves instead of hats
Her zipper's broken down the back
Waiting for a factory girl

Waiting for a girl and she gets me into fights
Waiting for a girl, we get drunk on Friday nights
She's a sight for sore eyes
Waiting for a factory girl

Waiting for a girl and she's got stains all down her
    dress
Waiting for a girl and my feet are getting wet
She ain't come out yet
Waiting for a factory girl

35
Family

Here's father, his heart screwed on
Yes, he got it I'm sure
'Cause he lost his life in an accident
Found his heart in the man next door

What exactly's gonna happen
When they do transplant the brain
Will my borrowed brain still be the same
Or will my daughter suffer so much more

Here comes the girl, she's got her head screwed on
But it ain't screwed on right
Her ambition is to be a prostitute
But the breaks just weren't right

What exactly's gonna happen
When her father finds out
That his virgin daughter has bordello dreams
And that he's the one she wants to try it out

There's ma, she's living dangerously
It's a cinch she'll try it again twice
She thinks she can run right in the whirlpool's edge
And stop herself just in time

What exactly's gonna happen
When she finds she fizzles out
The lovers will just be sucked into
To see what the colours of death are all about

Here's the son, has his legs a-screwed on
Yeah, they're screwed on pretty tight
But his brain is loose and it ain't no use
He's already lost the fight

What exactly's gonna happen
When he's finally realized
That he can't play guitar like E.G. Jim
Or write St. Augustine if he tried

That's what happens
When a family finds out
That they've been in orbit now for a thousand years
And need a thousand more to climb out

36
Faraway Eyes

I was driving home early Sunday morning through
Bakersfield listening to Gospel music on the
colored radio station, and the preacher said, "You
know you always have the Lord by your side."
I was so pleased to be informed of this, that I ran 20
red lights in his honor.
Thank you Jesus, thank you Lord.

I had an arrangement to meet a girl but I was kind of
late and I thought by the time I got there she'd be
off – she'd be off with the nearest truck driver she
could find:
Much to my surprise, there she was sitting in the
corner (a little bleary eyed – worse for wear and
tear) was the girl with faraway eyes.

So if you're down on your luck and you can't
harmonize,
Find a girl with faraway eyes
And if you're downright disgusted and life ain't worth
a dime,
Get a girl with faraway eyes.

Well the preacher kept right on saying that all I had
to do was send
Ten dollars to the Church of the Sacred Bleeding
Heart of Jesus
Located somewhere in Los Angeles, California, and
next week they'd say my prayer on the radio and
all my dreams would come true.
So I did and next week I got a prayer for the girl, well
you know what kind of eyes she's got . . .

So if you're down on your luck I know y'all
sympathize,
Find a girl with faraway eyes.
And if you're downright disgusted and life ain't worth
a dime
Get a girl with faraway eyes.
So if you're down on your luck I know y'all
sympathize,
Get a girl with faraway eyes.

Fingerprint File

Fingerprint file
You get me down
You get me running
Know my way around
Yes you do child

Fingerprint file
You get me down
You get me running
Keep me on the ground
Know my moves
Way ahead of time
List'ning to me
On your satellite

Feeling followed
Feeling tagged
Crossing water
Trying to wipe my tracks
And there's some little jerk in the FBI
Keeping papers on me
Six feet high
It gets me down
It gets me down
It gets me down

Better watch out
On your telephone
Wrong number
They know you ain't home
And there's some little jerk in the FBI
A-getting papers on me
Six feet high
It gets me down
It gets me down
It gets me down

Who's that man on the corner?
Not that corner over there
I don't know, well you better lay low

Keep on look out
Electric eyes
Rats on the sell out
Who gonna testify
You know my habits
Way ahead of time
List'ning to me
On your satellite
And there's some little jerk in the FBI
A-getting papers on me
Six feet high
It gets me down
It gets me down
It gets me down

Hallo baby
Mm – mm
Ah, yeah you know we ain't talkin' alone
Who's listening
But I don't really know
But you better tell the sis to keep out of sight
Cause I know they takin' pictures on the ultraviolet
    light
Yes
Aah but these days it's all secrecy not privacy
Shoot first, that's right, . . . you know
Bye bye
Who's listening
Right now, somebody is listening to you
Keeping their eyes peeled on you
Mmmh mmmh what a price, what a price to pay
All right
Good night, sleep tight.

Flight 505

Well I was happy here at home, I got ev'rything I
   need
Happy being on my ownsome living the life I lead
But suddenly it dawned on me that this was not my
life
So I just phoned the airline girl and said
Get me on flight number 505
Get me on flight number 505

Well I confirmed my reservation then I hopped a cab
No idea of my destination and feeling pretty bad
With my suitcase in my hand, in my head my new
life
And then I told the airline girl
Well get me on flight number 505
Get me on flight number 505

Well I sat right there in my seat well feeling like a
   king
With the whole world right at my feet of course I'll
   have a drink
But suddenly I saw that we never ever would arrive
He put the plane down in the sea
The end of flight number 505
The end of flight number 505

Fool To Cry

When I come home baby
And I've been working all night long
I put my daughter on my knee
And she say Daddy what's wrong?
She whisper in my ear so sweet
You know what she says?
She say Oo daddy you're a fool to cry
You're a fool to cry
And it makes me wonder why

You know I got a woman
And she live in a poor part of town
And I go see her sometimes
And we make love so fine
I put my head on her shoulder
She says tell me all your troubles
You know what she says?
She say Oo daddy you're a fool to cry
You're a fool to cry
And it makes me wonder why

She say Oooo daddy you're a fool to cry
Oooo daddy you're a fool to cry
Oooo daddy you're a fool to cry
Oooo daddy you're a fool to cry

Even my friends say to me sometimes
And make out like I don't understand them
You know what they say?
They say Oo daddy you're a fool to cry
You're a fool to cry
And it makes me wonder why

I'm a fool baby
I'm a fool baby
I'm a certified fool now

I want to tell ya
Gotta tell ya baby
I'm a fool baby
Certified fool for ya, mama, come on
I'm a fool, I'm a fool
I'm a fool

40
Get Off Of My Cloud

I live in an apartment on the ninety ninth floor of my
    block
And I sit at home lookin' out the window imaginin'
    the world has stopped
Then in flies a guy that's all dressed up just like a
    Union Jack
He says I've won five pounds if I have this kind of
    detergent pack
I said, hey you get off of my cloud, hey you get off of
    my cloud
Hey you get off of my cloud, don't hang around
'Cause two's a crowd on my cloud baby

The telephone is ringin' I say 'Hi it's me who's there
    on the line?'
A voice says 'Hi hullo. How are you?', 'Well I guess
    I'm doing fine'
He says 'It's three a.m. and there's too much noise,
    don't you people ever want to go to bed?'
Just cause you feel so good, do you have to drive me
    out of my head?'
I said, hey you get off of my cloud, hey you get off of
    my cloud
Hey you get off of my cloud, don't hang around
'Cause two's a crowd on my cloud baby

I was sick and tired, fed up with this and decided to
    take a drive down town
It was so very quiet and peaceful. There was nobody
    not a soul around
I laid myself out I was so tired and I started to dream
In the mornin' the parkin' tickets were just like flags
    stuck on my wind screen
I said, hey you get off of my cloud, hey you get off of
    my cloud
Hey you get off of my cloud, don't hang around
'Cause two's a crowd on my cloud baby

41
Gimmie Shelter

Oh, a storm is threat'ning my very life today
If I don't get some shelter, oh yeah I'm gonna fade
    away
War, children, it's just a shot away, it's just a shot
    away
War, children, it's just a shot away, it's just a shot
    away

See the fire is sweeping our very street today
Burns like a red coal carpet, mad bull lost its way
War, children, it's just a shot away, it's just a shot
    away
War, children it's just a shot away, it's just a shot
    away

Rape, murder, it's just a shot away, it's just a shot
    away
Rape, murder, it's just a shot away, it's just a shot
    away
Rape, murder, it's just a shot away, it's just a shot
    away
Mm the floods is threat'ning my very life today
Gimmie, gimmie shelter or I'm gonna fade away
War, children, it's just a shot away, it's just a shot
    away
It's just a shot away, it's just a shot away

I tell you
Love, sister, it's just a kiss away, it's just a kiss away
It's just a kiss away, it's just a kiss away

42
Goin' Home

Spending too much time away
I can't stand another day
Maybe you think I've seen the world
But I'd rather see my girl
I'm going home, I'm going home
I'm going home, I'm going home
I'm going home bam bam bam ba bam
Home bam bam bam ba back home
Yeah back home

All those letters ev'ry day
Maybe all right in their way
But I'd love to see your face
When I get home in their place
I'm going home, I'm going home
I'm going home, I'm going home
I'm going home, I'm going home
Home bam bam bam ba back home
Yeah back home

When you're three thousand miles away
I can never sleep the same
If I packed my things right now
I could be home in seven hours
I'm going home, I'm going home
I'm going home, I'm going home
I'm going home bam bam bam ba bam
Home bam bam bam ba back home
Yeah back home

43
Gomper

By the lake with lily flowers
While away the evening hours

To and fro she's gently gliding
On the glassy lake she's riding

She swims to the side
The sun sees her dried

The birds hover high
I stifle a cry

The birds hover high
She moans with a sigh

44

Good Times, Bad Times

There've been good times, there've been bad times
I've had my share of hard times too
But I lost my faith in the world
Honey when I lost you

Remember the good times we had together
Don't you want them back again
Tho' these hard times are bugging me now
I know now it's the same

There's gotta be trust in this world
Or it won't get very far
Well trusting someone
Or just gonna be war

45

Gotta Get Away

Baby, the truth is out so don't deny
Baby, to think I believed all your lies
Darlin', I can't stand to see your face
It's the truth ya understand
I got to get away, got to get away
Gotta gotta gotta get away
Got to get away

Baby, I don't want to live here no more
Baby, so I've torn your pictures off my wall
Darlin' this old room is fallin' in on me
You understand the truth then
I got to get away, got to get away
Gotta gotta gotta get away
Got to get away

Baby, oh how could you take away your clothes
Baby, don't screw up this old pot of gold
Darlin' this old room of mine is all so fair
You understand me dear
I got to get away, got to get away
Gotta gotta gotta get away
Got to get away

46

Grown Up Wrong

Well you grown up all wrong
Well you grown up all wrong
You come on too strong
Well you grown up all wrong
Well you were easy to fool
When you were in school
But you grown up all wrong

Really grown up on me
Well you grown up on me
Don't believe what I see
Well you grown up on me
Well you look so sweet
When you're in your seat
But you grown up on me

Well you grown up too fast
Well you grown up too fast
Don't forget about the past
Well you grown up too fast
Well you won't feel blue
When I'm through with you
But you grown up too fast

47

Hand Of Fate

The hand of fate is on me now
It picked me up and it knocked me down
I'm on the run, I'm prison bound
The hand of fate is a heavy now
I killed a man, I'm highway bound
The wheel of fortune keeps turning round
Turning round turning round
I should have known it was a one horse town
Cause my sweet girl was once his wife
And he had papers that the judge had signed
The wind blew hard it was a stormy night
He shot me once but I shot him twice
The hand of fate is on me now
It picked me up and it kicked me right down
It kicked me right down it kicked me right down

I had to save her life yeh
I gunned him twice yeh
And I watched him die
Watch out boy
Yeh I watched him die

He was a barroom man the violent kind
He had no love for that girl of mine
And then one day in a drinking bout
He swore he'd throw me right out of town
The hand of fate is on me now
I shot that man
I put him underground
I put him underground
I put him underground
Yes I did

I'm on the run
I hear the hounds
My luck is up
My chips are down
So goodbye baby so long now
Wish me luck I'm going to need it child
The hand of fate is on me now
Yeh it's too late baby it's too late baby

It's too late now
The hand of fate is on me now
Oh yeh hmm yeh yes it is
The hand of fate hangs a heavy now
It's a heavy now
Heavy now
The hand of fate is a heavy now
It picked me up and it knocked me down
It picked me up and it knocked me down

48
Happy

Well I never kept a dollar past sunset
It always burned a hole in my pants
Never made a schoolmama happy
Never blew a second chance

I need a love to keep me happy
I need a love to keep me happy
Baby, baby, keep me happy
Baby, baby, keep me happy

Always took candy from strangers
Didn't wanna get me no trade
Never want to be like papa
Working for the boss every night and day

I need a love to keep me happy
I need a love to keep me happy
Baby, baby, keep me happy
Baby, baby, keep me happy

Never got a flash out of cocktails
When I get some flesh off the bone
Never got a lift out of Lear Jets
When I can fly way back home

I need a love to keep me happy
I need a love to keep me happy
Baby, baby, won't you keep me happy
Baby, baby, won't you keep me happy

49
Have You Seen Your Mother, Baby

Have you seen your mother, baby, standing in the
    shadow?
Have you had another baby standing in the shadow
I'm glad I opened your eyes
The have nots would have tried to freeze you in ice

Have you seen your brother, baby, standing in the
    shadow?
Have you had another baby standing in the shadow
I was just passing the time
I'm all alone, won't you give all your sympathy
    to mine

Tell me a story about how you adore me
How we live in the shadow, how we see through the
    shadow
How we glimpse through the shadow, how we tear at
    the shadow
How we hate in the shadow and love in your
    shadowy life

Have you seen your lover, baby, standing in the
    shadow?
Have you had another baby standing in the shadow
Where have you been all your life?
Talking about all the people who would try anything
    twice

Have you seen your mother, baby, standing in the
    shadow?
Have you had another baby standing in the shadow
You take your choice at this time
The brave old world or the slide to the depths
    of decline

50

Heart Of Stone

There've been so many girls that I've known
I've made so many cry
And still I wonder why
Here comes the little girl
I see her walking down the street
She's all by herself
Trying so hard to please
But she'll never break
Never break never break
Never break this heart of stone
Oh no no this heart of stone

What's different about her? I don't really know
No matter how I try
I just can't make her cry
But she'll never break
Never break never break
Never break this heart of stone
Oh no no this heart of stone

Don't keep on looking that same old way
If you try acting sad
You'll only make me glad
Better listen little girl
You go walking down the street
I ain't got no love
I ain't the kind to meet
But you'll never break
Never break never break
Never break this heart of stone
Oh no no
You'll never break this heart of stone

51

Hey Negrita

I say hey Negrita
Hey now
Move your body
Move your mouth

Shake lady
Way down south
Shake baby
In your home town

Hey Negrita
Hey now
Hey conchita
Shake it up now
Ah yeah
Do it up now

Mueva las carreras
Do it up now
Flash of gold in your ears child
Flash of gold in your eyes
Saw the gleam in your mouth
Saw the steel in your thighs

Come si chiama, what's your game?
I'm just a poor man, what's your name?
Shake your body, do it up now
Shake your body, move it up now

Baté las caderas, do it up now
Just a momentita, not so fast
I need money for my need is fast

Listen, I'm a poor man, my pay is low
Here's one last dollar and then we go
One last dollar, I've got my pride
I'm gonna call ya boss, boy, gonna tan your hide

52
Hide Your Love

Sometimes I'm up, sometimes I'm down
Sometimes I'm falling on the ground
Why do you hide, why do you hide your love, baby
Now look here, baby, you sure look sweet
But you've been sleeping out on the street

Why do you hide, why do you hide your love
Why do you hide it, baby, why do you hide your love

Oh, babe, I'm sinking, I wanna cry
Well, I been drinking, but now I'm dry
Why do ya hide, why do ya hide your love
Now look here, baby, you sure look cheap
I make it, mama, seven days a week
Why do ya hide, where do ya hide ya love
Why do you hide it, baby
Hide from the man that you love

Oh yeah, oh yeah
Oh yeah, oh yeah
Why do you hide, why do you hide ya love
C'mon, c'mon, c'mon
C'mon, c'mon, c'mon

Oh Lord, I'm reaching, reaching high
Oh babe, I'm falling right out the sky
Why do ya hide, where do ya hide ya love
Why do ya hide it baby
Hide from the man that you love
Oh yeah, oh yeah
Oh yeah, oh yeah
Why do ya hide, why do ya hide your love
Why do ya hide it baby
Hide from the man that you love

53
High And Dry

High and dry, well I'm up here with no warning
High and dry, well I couldn't get a word in
High and dry oh what a way to go
She left me standing here just high and dry

One minute I was up there standing by her side
The next I was down here well left out of the ride
High and dry oh what a way to go
She left me standing here just high and dry

Anything I wish for I only had to ask her
I think she found out it was money I was after
High and dry oh what a weird let down
She left me standing here just high and dry

Lucky that I didn't have any love towards her
Next time I'll make sure that the girl will be much
poorer
High and dry oh what a way to go
She left me standing here just high and dry

54

Honky Tonk Women

I met a ginsoaked barroom queen in Memphis
She tried to take me upstairs for a ride
She had to heave me right across her shoulder
'Cos I just can't seem to drink you off my mind
It's the honky tonk women
Gimme, gimme, gimme the honky tonk blues

I laid a divorcee in New York City
I had to put up some kind of a fight
The lady then she covered me with roses
She blew my nose and then she blew my mind
It's the honky tonk women
Gimme, gimme, gimme the honky tonk blues

It's the honky tonk women
Gimme, gimme, gimme the honky tonk blues

55

Hot Stuff

Hot stuff
Hot stuff
Hot stuff
Hot stuff
Can't get enough
Hot stuff
Hot stuff
Hot stuff
Hot stuff
Can't get enough
That music is mighty fine
Hot stuff

Hot stuff
I can't get enough
I can't get enough
I can't get enough
That music is mighty mighty fine
Hot stuff

Hot stuff
Can't get enough
Hot stuff
Play it rough
Can't get enough

'Cause music is what I want
To keep my body always movin' yeah
Shake it up
Hot stuff
Ev'ry day I need another dose
I can't stand it when the music stops
Hot stuff

Everybody on the dance floor
You know what I'm talking about
Music make you forget all your troubles
Make you sing and make it tell the whole wide world
So what, hot stuff, shake it up

I want to tell all my friends in London
There ain't nothing wrong with you

But you'd better shape up
Shake it up, you're hot stuff

All the people in New York City
I know you're going broke
But I know you're tough
Yeah, you're hot stuff, hot stuff

To everybody in Jamaica that's working in the sun
You're hot, you're hot, you're hot stuff
Shake it up, shake it up
Hot stuff, hot stuff

56

I Am Waiting

I am waiting, I am waiting, oh yeah, oh yeah
I am waiting, I am waiting, oh yeah, oh yeah
Waiting for someone to come out of somewhere
Waiting for someone to come out of somewhere

You can't hold out, you can't hold out, oh yeah,
    oh yeah
You can't hold out, you can't hold out, oh yeah,
    oh yeah
Waiting for someone to come out of somewhere
Waiting for someone to come out of somewhere

See it come along and don't know where it's from
Oh, yes, we will find out
Well it happens all the time
It's censored from our mind, we'll find out

Slow or fast, slow or fast, oh yeah, oh yeah
End at last, end at last, oh yeah, oh yeah
Waiting for someone to come out of somewhere
Waiting for someone to come out of somewhere

Stand up coming hears and destilation fears
Oh, yes, we will find out
Well like a withered stone
Fears will piece your bones, you'll find out

Oh we're waiting, oh we're waiting, oh yeah, oh yeah
Oh we're waiting, oh we're waiting, oh yeah, oh yeah
Waiting for someone to come out of somewhere
Waiting for someone to come out of somewhere

57

I Got The Blues

As I stand by your flame
I get burned once again
Feeling low down and blue

As I sit by the fire
Of your warm desire
I've got the blues for you, yeah

Every night you've been away
I've sat down and I have prayed
That you're safe in the arms of a guy
Who will bring you alive
Won't drag you down with abuse

In the silk sheet of time
I will find peace of mind
Love is a bed full of blues
And I've got the blues for you
And I've got the blues for you
And I've got burned up
And I'll tear my hair out
I'm gonna tear my hair out just for you
If you don't believe what I'm saying at
3 o'clock in the morning baby
I'm singing my song for you

58

If You Can't Rock Me

The band's on stage and it's one of those nights
Oh yeah
The drummer thinks that he is dynamite
Oh yeah
You lovely ladies in your leather and lace
A thousand lips I would love to taste
I got one heart and it hurts like hell

If you can't rock me somebody will
If you can't rock me somebody will

Now who's that black girl in the bright blue hair
Oh yeah
Now don't you know that it's rude to stare
Oh yeah
I'm not so green but I'm feelin' so fresh
I simply love to put her to the test
She's so alive and she's dressed to kill

If you can't rock me somebody will
If you can't rock me somebody will
If you can't rock me somebody will

Now I ain't lookin' for no pretty face
Oh no
Or for some hooker working roughish trade
And there ain't nothing like a perfect mate
And I ain't lookin' for no wedding cake
But I been talking 'bout it much too long
I think I better sing just one more song
I've got one heart and it hurts like hell
I'm simply dying for some thrills and spills
Oh yeah

If you can't rock me
If you can't rock me
Ah somebody will

59

If You Let Me

You don't really understand
How it feels to be your man
You're just nice to have around, girl
But I'll let you guess
You can get me
If you let me oh yes

It's nice to talk to you today
It's very pleasant anyway
Is this as far as you go, girl
Could I let you guess
You can get me
If you let me oh yes

You can get me
If you let me oh yes

Yes, you're younger than I thought
You're so tall and I'm so short
It doesn't matter anyhow
Could I let you guess
You can get me
If you let me oh yes

It's a brand new thing for me
Loving you so physic'lly
The time has come to say goodbye
But I'll let you guess
You can get me
If you let me oh yes

If You Really Want To Be My Friend

If you really want to be my friend
Let me live it up
Like I used to do
If you really want to understand
Me there's some givin' up
We gotta do

I know that ev'rybody wants to be your man
I don't want to tie you up
Go ahead you're free
And I never want to scar you with my brand
We could live it up
Just you and me

If you really want to understand a man
Let him off the lead
Sometimes set him free
If you really want to be my friend
Give me the look of love
Not jealousy

I know you think that life is a thriller
You play the vamp I play the killer
No baby what's the use of fighting
By the last reel we'll be cryin', cryin', cryin'

If you really want to be a man
Get your nails out of my back
Stop using me

You know I really want to be your friend
Just a little faith is all we need
I just want no dog eat dog world for you and me
Get your nails out
Stop bleedin' me

Stop bleedin' me
You know
People tell me you were a vulture
Say you're a sore in a cancer culture
Aah but you got a little charm around you
I'll be there when they finally hound ya hound ya
   hound ya
Ooooh yeah mmmmmmmmmmmm

And I really want to understand you, baby
I, I yea

I wanna try to give you a helping hand
Yes I do
Wah yea
Wah yea
I wanna push you when you're up
And pull you when you're down

I tell you something
That love, love can't thrive on jealousy
Wah no
Wah no
And I really try to understand you, baby
Yes I do
Cause understanding is something everybody needs
Wah yea
I really want to be your friend

And I love ya
I love ya yes I do

61
I'm All Right

I wanna tell you something baby
That you don't know
No, you don't know
Gonna tell you
Gonna listen to me
'Cos it's all right

It's all right it's all right
It's all right it's all right
It's all right it's all right
It's all right it's all right
All night long all night long
All night long all night long
It's all right it's all right
All day through it's all right
All day through be all right
Be all right be all right
Be all right be all right

Do you feel it?
Do you? Do you feel it?
Do you? Do you, do you feel it?
Do you feel it baby?
Do you feel it baby?
Do you feel it?
Come on come on

Come on, come on, come on, come on, baby
Come on, come on, come on, come on, baby
Come on, come on, come on, come on, baby
Come on, come on, come on, come on, baby
Come on, come on, come on, come on
All right all right
It's all right it's all right
It's all right it's all right
It's all right it's all right
It's all right it's all right
It's all right

62
I'm Free

I'm free to do what I want any old time
I'm free to do what I want any old time
So love me hold me love me hold me
I'm free any old time to get what I want

I'm free to sing my song knowing it's out of trend
I'm free to sing my song knowing it's out of trend
So love me hold me love me hold me
'Cause I'm free any old time to get what I want

So love me hold me love me hold me
I'm free any old time to get what I want

I'm free to choose who I see any old time
I'm free to bring who I choose any old time
Love me hold me love me hold me
I'm free any old time to get what I want

63

I'm Going Down

Hey babe, what's wrong with you, girl
I have come around ringing your front door bell
Though our love fall down in dark clouds

Alright

Here we go down now There's nothing for me but the
powers that be
I know I, I know I, I know I, I know that you're down

64

In Another Land

In another land where the breeze and the trees
And the flowers grow blue
I stop and hold your hand and the grass grew high
And the feathers floated by
I stood and held your hand
And nobody else's hand will ever do
Nobody else will do

And I awoke was this some kind of joke
Much to my surprise I opened my eyes

We walked across the sand and the sea and the sky
And the castles were blue
I stop and hold your hand and the spray through the
    pine
And the feathers floated by
I stood and held your hand
And nobody else's hand will ever do
Nobody else will do

And I awoke was this some kind of joke
Much to my surprise I opened my eyes

We heard the trumpets blow and the sky turned grey
And I had to take this day
But I didn't know how I came to be there
When I'm fast asleep in bed
I stood and held your hand
And nobody else's hand will ever do
Nobody else will do

And I awoke was this some kind of joke
Much to my surprise I opened my eyes

65

It's Not Easy

It's not easy
It's not easy living on your own
It's not easy
It's not easy living on your own
And it's hard (it's not easy)
Yes it's hard (it's not easy)
It's a very hard thing
It's not easy
It's not easy living on your own

All of the things that she used to do
If they're done now well they're done by you
It seems a big failing in a man
To take his girl for granted if he can

It's a hard (it's not easy)
Yes it's hard (it's not easy)
It's a very hard thing
It's not easy
It's not easy living on your own

There's no place where you can call home
You've got me running like a cat in a thunderstorm
Just a big bed and a telephone
Like the last remnants of a stately home

It's a hard (it's not easy)
Yes it's hard (it's not easy)
It's a very hard thing
It's not easy
It's not easy living on your own

It's a hard (it's not easy)
Yes it's hard (it's not easy)
It's a very hard thing
It's not easy
It's not easy living on your own

Sit here thinking with your head on fire
Go think the same thing you never tire
Imagining the glow of her long clean hair
As she goes to sit on her own high chair

It's a hard (it's not easy)
Yes it's hard (it's not easy)
It's a very hard thing
It's not easy
It's not easy living on your own

66

It's Only Rock 'N' Roll

If I could stick my pen in my heart
I'd spill it all over the stage
Would it satisfy ya
Or would it slide on by ya
Or would you just think the boy is strange
Ain't he stra-ya-yange

If I could win you
If I could sing you a love song so divine
Would it be enough for your cheating heart
If I broke down and cried
If I cr-yi-yied

I said I know it's only rock 'n' roll but I like it
I said I know it's only rock 'n' roll but I like it
But I like it I like it yes I do
Well I like it I like it I like it
I said can't you see this old boy's getting lonely

If I could stick a knife in my heart
Suicide right on the stage
Would it be enough for your teenage lust
Would it help ease the pain
Ease your brain

If I could dig deep down in my heart
Feelings would flood on the page
Would it satisfy ya
Would it slide on by ya
Would you think the boy's insane
He's insa-ya-yane

I said I know it's only rock 'n' roll but I like it
I said I know it's only rock 'n' roll but I like it
But I like it I like it yes I do
Well I like it I like it I like it
I said can't you see this old boy's getting lonely

I bet you think that you're the only girl around
I bet you think that you're the only woman in town

I said I know it's only rock 'n' roll but I like it
I said I know it's only rock 'n' roll but I like it
But I like it I like it yes I do
Well I like it I like it I like it
I said can't you see this boy's getting lonely

Jigsaw Puzzle

There's a tramp sitting on my doorstep
Trying to waste his time
With his mentholated sandwich
He's a walking clothesline
But here comes the bishop's daughter
On the other side
And she looks a trifle jealous
She's been an outcast all her life

Me I'm waiting so patiently lying on the floor
I'm just tryin' to do my jigsaw puzzle
Before it rains any more

Oh, the gangster looks so fright'ning
With his luger in his hand
But when he gets home to his children
He's a family man
But when it comes to the nitty gritty
He can shove in his knife
Yes, he really looks quite religious
He's been an outlaw all his life

Me I'm waiting so patiently lying on the floor
I'm just tryin' to do my jigsaw puzzle
Before it rains any more

Me I'm waiting so patiently lying on the floor
I'm just trying' to do my jigsaw puzzle
Before it rains any more

Oh, the singer looks so angry
At being thrown to the lions
And the bass player looks so nervous
About the girls outside
And the drummer he was shattered
Trying to keep on time
And the guitar player looks damaged
They've been outcasts all their lives

Me I'm waiting so patiently lying on the floor
I'm just tryin' to do my jigsaw puzzle
Before it rains any more

And as twenty thousand grandmas
Wave their hankies in the air
All burning up their pensions
And shouting, 'It's not fair'
There's a regiment of soldiers
Standing, looking on
And the Queen is bravely shouting
'What the hell is going on?'
With a blood curdling tallyho
She charged into the ranks
And blessed all those grandmas
Who, with their dying breath, screamed, 'Thanks'

Me, I'm waiting so patiently with my woman on the
    floor
I'm just tryin' to do my jigsaw puzzle
Before it rains any more

68

Jivin' Sister Fanny

Jivin' Sister Fanny that's the name of the girl I love
    uh uh huh
She even got me goin' outta town down the wrong
    highway uh huh huh
She got me walkin' round she got me goin' down
Hey, said the policeman, get your sister out of town
Oh oh chile, you got me walkin' down the wrong
    highway hey hey hey
Now Jivin' Sister Fanny you got a brain like a girl
    insane uh huh huh
She got my money and she broke my electric guitar
    huh huh huh
She got me walkin' round she got me goin' down
You got me walking down the wrong highway oh oh
    oh oh

69

Jumpin' Jack Flash

I was born in a crossfire hurricane
And I howled at my ma in the driving rain
But it's all right now
In fact it's a gas
But it's all right
I'm Jumpin' Jack Flash
It's a gas, gas, gas

I was raised by a toothless bearded hag
I was schooled with a strap across my back
But it's all right now
In fact it's a gas
But it's all right
I'm Jumpin' Jack Flash
It's a gas, gas, gas

I was drowned. I was washed up and left for dead
I fell down to my feet and I saw they bled
And I frowned at the crumbs of a crust of bread
I was crowned with a pike right through my head
But it's all right now
In fact it's a gas
But it's all right
I'm Jumpin' Jack Flash
It's a gas, gas, gas

70
Just Want To See His Face

That's all right, that's all right, that's all right
Sometimes you feel like trouble, sometimes you feel
    down
Let this music relax your mind, let this music relax
    your mind
Stand up and be counted, can I get a witness

Sometimes you need somebody, if you have
    somebody to love
Sometimes you ain't got nobody and you want
    somebody to love
Then you don't want to walk and talk about Jesus
You just want to see His face

You don't want to walk and talk about Jesus
You just want to see His face

71
Lady Jane

My sweet Lady Jane
When I see you again
Your servant am I
And will humbly remain
Just heed this plea my love
On bended knees my love
I pledge myself to Lady Jane

My dear Lady Anne
I've done what I can
I must take my leave
For promised I am
This play is run my love
Your time has come my love
I've pledged my troth to Lady Jane

Oh my sweet Marie
I wait at your ease
The sands have run out
For your lady and me
Wedlock is nigh my love
Her station's right my love
Life is secure with Lady Jane

72
Let It Bleed

Well we all need someone we can lean on
And if you want it, well you can lean on me
Well, we all need someone we can lean on
And if you want it well you can lean on me

She said, 'My breasts they will always be open
Baby, you can rest your weary head on me
And there will always be a space in my parking lot
When you need a little coke and sympathy'

Yeah we all need someone we can dream on
And if you want it, well you can dream on me
Yeah, we all need someone we can cream on
And if you want to well you can cream on me

I was dreaming of a steel guitar engagement
When you drink my health in scented jasmine tea
You knifed me in my dirty filthy basement
With that jaded faded junky nurse, oh what pleasant
   company

We all need someone we can feed on
And if you want it well you can feed on me
Take my arm, take my leg
Oh, baby, don't you take my head

We all need someone we can bleed on
And if you want it, baby, well you can bleed on me
We all need someone we can bleed on
And if you want it why don't you bleed on me

Get it on, rider
Get it on, rider
Get it on, rider you can bleed all over me

73
Let It Loose

Who's that woman on your arm
All dressed up to do you harm?
And I'm hip to what she'll do
Give her just about a month or two

Bit off more than I could chew
And I knew what it was leading to
Some things well I can't refuse
One of them the bedroom blues

She delivers right on time
I can't resist a corny line
But take the shine right off your shoes
Carrying the bedroom blues
Oo oo ooo ooo ooo

In the bar you're getting drunk
I ain't in love I ain't in luck
Hide the switch and shut the light
Let it all come down tonight

Maybe your friends think I'm just a stranger
Some face you'll never see no more
Let it all come down tonight
Keep those tears hid out of sight
Let it loose
Let it all come down
Let it loose
Let it all come down
Let it loose
Let it all come down

74

Let's Spend The Night Together

Don't you worry what's on your mind
(Oh my, da da da da da da da)
I'm in no hurry I can take my time
(Oh my, da da da da da da da)
I'm going red and my tongue's getting tied
I'm off my head and my mouth's getting dry
(I'm high, but I try, try, try- oh my)
Let's spend the night together
Now I need you more than ever
Let's spend the night together now

I feel so strong that I can't disguise
(Oh my, let's spend the night together)
But I just can't apologise
(Oh no, let's spend the night together)
Don't hang me up and don't let me down
We could have fun just grooving around
(Around and around oh- my, my)
Let's spend the night together
Now I need you more than ever
Let's spend the night together
Let's spend the night together
Now I need you more than ever

You know I'm smiling, baby
You need some guiding, baby
I'm just deciding, baby
Now I need you more than ever
Let's spend the night together
Let's spend the night together now

This doesn't happen to me ev'ry day
(Oh my, let's spend the night together)
No excuses offered anyway
(Oh my, let's spend the night together)
I'll satisfy your ev'ry need
And now I know you will satisfy me
(Oh my, my, my- oh my)
Let's spend the night together
Now I need you more than ever
Let's spend the night together now

75

Lies

Lies – dripping off ya mouth like dirt
Lies – lies in every step ya walk
Lies – whispered sweetly in my ear
Lies – how do I get out of here?
Why – why you have to be so cruel
Lies, lies, I ain't such a fool

Lies – lies in my Poppas looks
Lies – lies in my history books
Lies – lies like they teach in class
Lies, lies, lies I catch on way too fast
Fire, fire upon your wicked tongue
Lies, lies, lies you're trying to spoil my fun.

Lies – lies you dirty Jezebel
Why, why, why, why don't you go to Hell?
Why – why you think me such a fool
Lies, lies, lies, honey that's ya rules!

Lies, lies, lies, lies, lies, lies
Lies, lies, lies, lies, lies, lies

Little By Little

Live With Me

Tried to trail you last night baby, trail you in my car
But I was afraid of what I was lookin' for
And little by little I'm losin' my love for you
Yeah little by little I've found out you're not true

I try not to bear a grudge a girl gotta hitch a ride
Things ain't been the same since my mother died
Yeah little by little I'm losin' my love for you
Yeah little by little I've found out you're not true

I've got nasty habits
I take tea at three
Yes, and the meat I eat for dinner
Must be hung up for a week
My best friend he shoots water rats
And feeds them to his geese
Doncha think there's a place for you in between the
    sheets?
Come on now, honey, we can build a home for three
Come on now, honey, don't you want to live with
    me?

And there's a score of hare-brained children
They are a-locked in the nursery
They got earphone heads. They got dirty necks
They're so twentieth century
Well, they queue up for the bathroom
Round about seven thirty-five
But doncha think we need a woman's touch to make
    it come alive?
You'd look good prampushing down the High Street
Come on now, honey, don't you want to live with
    me?

Oh the servants they're so helpful, dear!
The cook she is a whore
Yes, the butler has a place for her
Behind the pantry door
The maid, she's French, she's got no sense
She's from the Crazy Horse
And when she strips, the chauffeur flips
The footman's eyes get crossed
Doncha think there's a place for us right across the
    street?
Doncha think there's a place for you in between the
    sheets?

Long, Long While

Baby baby been a long long time
Been a long long time been a long long time
I was wrong girl and you were right

Baby baby took a long long while
Took a long long while took a long long while
But I found out you were right

Still you have those happy eyes
I will try and apologise

Baby baby still the same old smile
Still the same old smile still the same old smile
I was so wrong and you were right

Still you have those happy eyes
I will try and apologise

Baby baby been a long long time
Been a long long time been a long long time
I was wrong girl and you were right

Baby baby won't you change your mind
Won't you change your mind won't you change your
    mind
I was wrong girl but not this time

Love In Vain

Well, I followed her to the station with a suitcase in
    my hand,
Yeah, I followed her to the station with a suitcase in
    my hand.
Well, it's hard to tell, it's hard to tell, but all true
    love's in vain.
When the train come in the station I looked her in
    the eye,
Well, the train come in the station and I looked her in
    the eye.
Well, I felt so sad and lonesome that I could not help
    but cry.
When the train left the station, it had two lights
    on behind,
Yeah, when the train left the station, it had two lights
    on behind,
Yeah, when the train left the station, it had two lights
    on behind.
Well, the blue light was my baby and the red light
    was my mind.
All my love's in vain. All, all my love's in vain.

80

Loving Cup

I'm the man on the mountain, come on up
I'm the plowman in the valley with a face full of mud
Yes, I'm fumbling and I know my car don't start
Yes, I'm stumbling and I know I play a bad guitar

Give me little drink from your loving cup
Just one drink and I'll fall down drunk

I'm the man who walks the hillside in the sweet
    summer sun
I'm the man that brings you roses when you ain't got
    none
Well, I can run and jump and fish, but I won't fight
You if you want to push and pull with me all night

Give me little drink from your loving cup
Just one drink and I'll fall down drunk

I feel so humble with you tonight, just sitting in front
    of the fire
See your face dancing in the flame, feel your mouth
    kissing me again
What a beautiful buzz, what a beautiful buzz
What a beautiful buzz, what a beautiful buzz
Oh, what a beautiful buzz, what a beautiful buzz

Yes I am nitty gritty and my shirt's all torn
But I would love to spill the beans with you till dawn

Give me little drink from your loving cup
Just one drink and I'll fall down drunk

81

Luxury

I want a real fine car
Fly Miami too
All the rum I want to drink it
All your whiskey too
My woman need a new dress
My daughter got to go to school
I'm working so hard, I'm working for the company
I'm working so hard to keep you in the luxury

And you can't call me lazy
On a seven day a week
Make a million for the Texans
Twenty dollar me
Yes I want a gold ring
Riding in a limousine
I'm working so hard, I'm working for the company
I'm working so hard to keep you in the luxury

Now listen I'm a proud man
Not a beggar walking on the street
I'm working so hard to keep you from the poverty
I'm working so hard to keep you in the luxury

I'm working so hard
I'm working so hard
Harder harder
Working working working working

I think it's such a strange thing
Giving me concern
Half the world got a nothing
The other half got money to burn
My woman need a new dress
My daughter got to go to school
I'm working so hard, I'm working for the company
I'm working so hard, I'm working so hard, oh yeah

Working on a Sunday
In refinery
Make a million for the Texans
Twenty dollar me

All the rum I want to drink it
I got responsibility
I'm working so hard to keep you from the poverty
I'm working so hard, I'm working for the company

Harder harder
Harder harder
Harder harder
Harder harder

Melody

Memo From Turner

Melody Melody
It was her second name
Melody
It was her second name
Melody
It was her second name

I came home one morning
About a quarter to three
I'm banging on my door
Cause I just lost my key
Open up baby you got someone else inside
I'm gonna come and get you dead or alive

Melody
It was her second name

I took her out dancing
But she drank away my cash
She said I'm gonna fix my face
Don't you worry I'll be back
I'm looking for her high and low
Like a mustard for a ham
She was crashed out in the bathroom
In the arms of my best friend

Melody
It was her second name

Then one day she left me
She took everything that moved
She took my car, my trailer home
She took my Sunday boots
My nose is on her trail
I'm gonna catch her by surprise
And then I'm gonna have the pleasure
To roast that child alive

Melody
It was her second name

Didn't I see you down in San Antone on a hot and
    dusty night?
You were eating eggs in Sammy's when the black
man there drew his knife
Or you drowned that Jew in Rampton as he washed
    his sleeveless shirt
You know that Spanish speaking gentleman, the one
    we all call Kurt
Come now, gentlemen, I know there's some mistake
How forgetful I'm becoming now you fixed your
    business straight

I remember you in Hemlock Road in nineteen
    fifty-six
You were a faggy little leather boy with a smaller
    piece of stick
You were a lashing smashing hunk of man, your
    sweat shine sweet and strong
Your organ's working perfectly but there's a part
    that's not screwed on

Weren't you at the Coke Convention back in
    nineteen sixty-five?
You're the misbred grey executive I've seen heavily
    advertised
You're the great grey man whose daughter licks
    policemen's buttons clean
You're the man who squats behind the man who
works the soft machine
Come now, gentlemen, your love is all I crave
You'll still be in the circus when I'm laughing,
    laughing in my grave

When the old men do the fighting and the young men
    all look on
And the young girls eat their mother's meat from
    tubes of plasticon
Be wary of these my gentle friends of all the skin
    you breed
To have that tasty habit, it ain't the hands that bleed

So remember who you say you are but keep your
    noses clean
Boys will be boys and play with toys so be strong
    with your beast
Oh Rosie dear, doncha think it's queer so stop me if
    you please
The baby is dead, my lady said 'You gentlemen, will
you all work for me?'

Memory Motel

Hannah honey was a peachy kind of girl
Her eyes were hazel and her nose was slightly curved
We spent a lonely night at the Memory Motel
It's on the ocean I guess you know it well
It took a starry night to steal my breath away
Down on the waterfront her hair all drenched
    in spray

Hannah baby was a honey of a girl
Her eyes were hazel her teeth were slightly curved
She took my guitar and she began to play
She sang a song to me it stuck right in my brain

You're just a memory of a love that used to be
You're just a memory of a love that used to mean so
    much to me
She got a mind of her own and she use it well
Well she's one of a kind
She got a mind of her own and she use it mighty fine

She drove a pick-up truck painted green and blue
The tires were wearing thin she done a mile or two
And when I asked her where she headed for
(Back up to Boston I'm singing in a bar)
I got to fly today on down to Baton Rouge
My nerves are shot already the road ain't all that
    smooth
Across in Texas is the rose of San Antone
I keep on a feeling that gnawing in my bones

You're just a memory of a love that used to mean so
    much to me
You're just a memory of a love that used to mean so
    much to me
You're just a memory girl you're just a sweet
    old memory
And it used to mean so much to me

Sha la laa la sha la laa la sha la laa la sha la laa la

You're just a memory of a love that used to mean so
    much to me

She got a mind of her own and she use it well
Mighty fine she's one of a kind
She's got a mind of her own
She's one of a kind and she use it well

On the seventh day my eyes were all aglaze
We been ten thousand miles and been in fifteen states
Every woman seemed to fade out of my mind
I hit the bottle and I hit the sack and cried
What's all this laughter on the twenty-second floor?
It's just some friends of mine and they're busting
    down the doors

It's been a lonely night at the Memory Motel

You're just a memory girl just a memory
And it used to mean so much to me
You're just a memory girl you're just a memory
And it used to mean so much to me
You're just a memory girl you're just a sweet old
    memory
And it used to mean so much to me
You're just a memory of a love that used to mean so
    much to me
She's got a mind of her own and she use it well yeh
Well she's one of a kind

Midnight Rambler

Miss Amanda Jones

Did you hear about the midnight rambler?
Ev'rybody got to go
Did you hear about the midnight rambler
The one that shut the kitchen door?

He don't give a hoot of a warning
A-wrapped up in a black cat cloak
He don't go in the light of the morning
He's split the time the cock'rel crows

A-talking 'bout the midnight gambler
The one you never seen before
A-talking 'bout the midnight gambler
Did you see him jump the garden wall?

A-sighing down the wind so sadly
A-listen and you hear him moan
Well I'm talking 'bout the midnight gambler
Ev'rybody got to go

A-did you hear about the midnight gambler?
Well honey, it's no rock and roll show
Well I'm talking 'bout the midnight rambler
Yeah, the one you never seen before

Well you heard about the Boston . . .
It's not one of those . . .
Well, talking 'bout the midnight . . .
The one who closed the bedroom door

I'm called the hit and run rape her in anger
The knifesharpened tippytoe
Or just the shoot 'em dead brainbell jangler
You know, the one you never seen before

So if you ever meet the midnight rambler
Padding down your marble hall
Well he's prowling like a proud black panther
You can say I told you so

Well won't you listen for the midnight rambler
Play it easy as you go
I'm going to smash down all your plateglass windows
Put a fist right thru' your steel plate door

Did you hear about the midnight rambler?
He'll leave his footprints up and down your hall
A-did you hear about the midnight gambler?
A-did you see me make my midnight call?

And if you ever catch the midnight rambler
I'll steal your mistress from under your nose
Well, go easy with your cold fandango
I'll stick my knife right down your throat, baby
And it hurts!

Down and down she goes
Little Miss Amanda Jones
I said down and down and down and down
She'd look really lovely at home
Till somebody gonna come up and ask her
To live happily ever after
Miss Amanda Jones

On and on she goes
Little Miss Amanda Jones
I said on and on and on and on
Just watch her as she grows
Don't want to say it very obviously
But she's losing her nobility
Miss Amanda Jones

Hey girl, don't you realise
The money invested in you
Hey girl, you've just got to find someone
Who'll really pull your family through

Up and up she goes
The Hon Amanda Jones
I said up and up and up and up
She looks quite delightfully stoned
She's the darling of the discotheque crowd
Of her lineage she's rightfully proud
Miss Amanda Jones

Hey girl, with your nonsense nose
Pointing right down at the floor
Hey girl, your suspender shows
And the girl behind you looks a bit unsure

Round and round she goes
Little Miss Amanda Jones
I said round and round and round and round
To the balls and dinners and shows
The little girl she just wonders about
Till it's time for her coming out
Miss Amanda Jones

87

Miss You

I've been holding out so long,
I've been sleeping all alone,
Lord, I miss you.
I've been hanging on the phone,
I've been sleeping all alone,
I want to kiss you

I've been haunted in my sleep,
You've been the star in all my dreams,
Lord, I miss you, child

I've been waiting in the hall,
Been waiting on your call when the phone rings,
It's just some friends of mine that say: "Hey,
what's the matter, man? We're gonna come around at
12:00 with some Puerto Rican girls that are just
dying to meet you.
We're gonna bring a case of wine – Hey, let's go
    mess and fool around, you know like we used to!"

Ooooh, everybody waits so long
Ooooh, Baby why you wait so long
Won't you come on, come home!

I've been walking Central Park, singing after dark
People think I'm crazy
Stumbling on my feet, shuffling through the street
Asking people, "What's the matter with you, boy?"
Sometimes I want to say to myself, sometimes
    I say . . .
Hooooohooooo Hooooohooooo Hooooohooooo

I guess I'm lying to myself – it's you and no one else
Lord, I won't miss you, child
You've just been blotting out my mind – fooling on
    my time
No, I won't miss you, baby
Lord, I miss your touch . . .

88

Monkey Man

I'm a fleabit peanut monkey
And all my friends are junkies
That's not really true
I'm a cold Italian pizza
I could use a lemon squeezer
What d'you do?
I've been bitten, I've been tossed around
By ev'ry she-rat in this town
Have you, babe?
Well I am just a monkey man
I'm glad you are a monkey woman too

I was bitten by a boar
I was gouged and I was gored
But I pulled on through
Yes, I'm a sack of broken eggs
I always have an unmade bed
Don't you
Well I hope we're not too messianic
Or a trifle too satanic
We love to play the blues
But when I am just a monkey man
I'm glad you are a monkey woman too

Moonlight Mile

When the wind blows and the rain feels cold
With a head full of snow, with a head full of snow
In the window there's a face you know
Don't the nights pass slow, don't the nights pass slow
The sound of strangers sending nothing to my mind
Just another mad mad day on the road
I am just living to be lying by your side
But I am just about a moonlight mile on the road

Made a rag pile of my shiny clothes
Gonna warm my bones, gonna warm my bones
I got silence on my radio
Let the air waves flow, let the air waves flow
For I am sleeping under strange strange skies
Just another mad mad day on the road
My dreams is fading down the railway lines
I'm just about a moonlight mile on down the road

I'm hiding sister and I'm dreaming
I'm riding down your moonlight mile
I'm hiding baby and I'm dreaming
I'm riding down your moonlight mile
I'm riding down your moonlight mile
Yea, I'm coming home
I'm just about a moonlight mile on down the road
Down the road down the road
Yea, baby

Mother's Little Helper

What a drag it is getting old

Kids are different today, I hear ev'ry mother say
Mother needs something today to calm her down
And though she's not really ill, there's a little
    yellow pill
She goes running for the shelter of a mother's little
    helper
And it helps her on her way, gets her through her
    busy day

Things are different today, I hear ev'ry mother say
Cooking fresh food for a husband's just a drag
So she buys an instant cake, and she burns her
    frozen steak
And goes running for the shelter of a mother's little
    helper
And two help her on her way, gets her through her
    busy day

Doctor please some more of these
Outside the door, she took four more
What a drag it is getting old

Men just aren't the same today, I hear ev'ry mother
say
They just don't appreciate that you get tired
They're so hard to satisfy, you can tranquilize
    your mind
So go running for the shelter of a mother's little
    helper
And four help you through the night, help to
    minimise your plight

Doctor please some more of these
Outside the door, she took four more
What a drag it is getting old

Life's just much too hard today, I hear ev'ry
    mother say
The pursuit of happiness just seems a bore
And if you take more of those, you will get an
    overdose
No more running to the shelter of a mother's little
    helper
They just helped you on your way through your busy
    dying day

91

My Obsession

My obsession is your possession
Ev'ry piece that I can get
My obsession is your possession
Till my mouth is soaking wet
I think I blew it by confession
You can't dodge it, it's simple logic
You'd be better off with me
And you'll know it when you've lost it
Lonely

My obsession is your possession
Are you smiling in my way
My obsession is your possession
One that you should give away
Give it to me now I've no objection
I don't mind if it's unkind
And it's not my property
But I want it just to be mine
Exclusively

You need teaching you're a girl
There are things in this world
That need teaching with discretion
My profession

My obsession is your possession
Are you used to the idea?
My obsession is your possession
Do you feel at home right here?
You should relax is my impression
Didn't see you were so young
I could almost be your son
Please turn in my direction
No objection

92

19th Nervous Breakdown

You're the kind of person you meet at certain dismal
    dull affairs
Centre of a crowd talking much too loud running up
    and down the stairs
It seems to me that you've seen too much in too
    few years
And though you try you just can't hide your eyes are
    edged with tears
You better stop look around
Here it comes here it comes here it comes here
    it comes
Here it comes your nineteenth nervous breakdown

When you were a child you were treated kind
    but never brought up right
You were overspoilt with a thousand toys and still
    you cried all night
Your mother who neglected you owes a million
    dollars tax
Your father's still perfecting ways of making sealing
    wax
You better stop look around
Here it comes here it comes here it comes here it
    comes
Here it comes your nineteenth nervous breakdown

Oh who's to blame? The girl's just insane
Well nothing I do don't seems to work
It only seems to make matters worse. Oh please

You were still in school when you had that fool who
    really messed your mind
And after that you turned your back on treating
    people kind
On our first trip I tried so hard to rearrange your
    mind
But after a while I realised you were disarranging
    mine
You better stop look around
Here it comes here it comes here it comes here it
    comes

Here it comes your nineteenth nervous breakdown

Oh who's to blame? The girl's just insane
Well nothing I do don't seems to work
It only seems to make matters worse. Oh please

When you were a child you were treated kind but
    never brought up right
You were overspoilt with a thousand toys and still
    you cried all night
Your mother who neglected you owes a million
    dollars tax
Your father's still perfecting ways of making sealing
    wax
You better stop look around
Here it comes
Here it comes your nineteenth nervous breakdown

93

No Expectations

Take me to the station
And put me on a train
I've got no expectations
To pass through here again

Once I was a rich man
And now I am so poor
But never in my sweet short life
Have I felt like this before

Your heart is like a diamond
You throw your pearls at swine
And as I watched you leaving me
You packed my peace of mind

Our love was like the water
That splashes on a stone
Our love is like our music
It's here and then it's gone

So take me to the airport
And put me on a plane
I've got no expectations
To pass through here again

94

Now I've Got A Witness

Instrumental

95
Off The Hook

Sitting in my bedroom late last night
Climbed into bed and turned out the light
Tried to call my baby on the telephone
All I got was the busy tone
It's off the hook, it's off the hook
It's off the hook, it's off the hook
It's off the hook

Off it so long she upset my mind
Why is she talkin' such a long time
Maybe she's a sleepin' maybe she's ill
Phone's disconnected unpaid bill
It's off the hook, it's off the hook
It's off the hook, it's off the hook
It's off the hook

Don't wanna see her 'fraid of what I'd find
Tired of letting her upset me all the time
Back into bed started readin' my book
Take my phone right off the hook
It's off the hook, it's off the hook
It's off the hook, it's off the hook
It's off the hook

96
On With The Show

Good evening one and all
We're all so glad to see you here
We'll play your fav'rite songs
While you all soak up the atmosphere
We'll start with Old Man River
Then maybe Stormy Weather too
I'm sure you know just what to do
On with the show, good health to you

Please pour another glass
It's time to watch the cabaret
Your wife will never know
That you're not really working late
Your hostess here is Wendy
You'll find her very friendly too
And we don't care just what you do
On with the show, good health to you

And if by chance you find
That you can't make it anymore
We'll put you in a cab
And get you safely to the door
Oh, we've got all the answers
And we've got lovely dancers too
There's nothing else you have to do
On with the show, good health to you

You're all such lovely people
Dancing gaily round the floor
But if you have to fight, please
Take your troubles out the door
And now I say with sorrow
Until this time tomorrow, oh
We'll bid you all a fond adieu
On with the show, good health to you

100 Years Ago

Went out walking through the woods the other day
And the world was a carpet laid before me
The birds were humming and the air smelled sweet
   and strange
And it seemed like a hundred years ago

Mary and I would sit upon a gate
Just gazing at some dragon in the sky
What tender days we had no secrets hid away
Well it seemed about a hundred years ago

Now all my friends are wearing worried smiles
Living out a dream of what they was
Don't you think it's sometimes wise not to grow up

Went out walking through the woods the other day
Can't you see the furrows in my forehead
What tender days we had no secrets hid away
Now it seems about a hundred years ago

Now if you see me drinking bad red wine
Don't worry about this man that you love
Don't you think it's sometimes wise not to grow up

You're gonna miss this man and say goodbye
Yeah I warn you
You're gonna miss and say goodbye
Yeah I warn you
You're gonna kiss and say goodbye
Oh Lord I warn you
And please excuse me while I hide away
Call me lazybones ain't got no time to waste away
Lazybones ain't got no time to waste away
Don't you think don't you think
It's just about time to hide away yeah yeah

One More Try

You need some money in a hurry when things ain't
   right
You try to beg and borrow maybe start a fight
Your friends don't want to know you they just pass
   you by
So they couldn't be your friends because they
   wouldn't lie

Sit down shut up don't dare cry
Things'll get better if you really try
So don't you panic don't you panic give it one
   more try
So don't you panic don't you panic give it one
   more try

You've got a girl that doesn't think at all, she cries
The days and all the nights you try to satisfy
You bring her all the things she wants she don't
   improve
You think you'll give her up and tell her
   'maybe I'll move'

Sit down shut up don't dare cry
Things'll get better if you really try
So don't you panic don't you panic give it one
   more try
So don't you panic don't you panic give it one
   more try

Things don't matter easy come and go
And the thing that satisfies only time will show
You've got to know well what you want in your mind
'Cause it's better when you get it if you give it a try

Sit down shut up don't dare cry
Things'll get better if you really try
So don't you panic don't you panic give it one
   more try
So don't you panic don't you panic give it one
   more try

Out Of Time

You don't know what's going on
You've been away for far too long
You can't come back
And think you are still mine
You're out of touch my baby
My poor discarded baby
I said baby, baby,
You're out of time

Well baby, baby,
You're out of time
I said baby, baby,
You're out of time
Yes you are left out
Out of there without a doubt
'Cause baby, baby,
You're out of time

A girl who wants to run away
Discovers that she's had her day
It's no good you thinking
That you are still mine
You're out of touch my baby
My poor unfaithful baby
I said baby, baby
You're out of time

Well baby, baby,
You're out of time
I said baby, baby,
You're out of time
Yes you are left out
Out of there without a doubt
'Cause baby, baby,
You're out of time

You thought you were a clever girl
Giving up your social whirl
But you can't come back
And be the first in line
You're obsolete my baby
My poor oldfashioned baby
I said baby, baby
You're out of time

Well baby, baby,
You're out of time
I said baby, baby
You're out of time
Yes you are left out
Out of there without a doubt
'Cause baby, baby
You're out of time

Paint It Black

I see a red door and I want it painted black
No colours anymore I want them to turn black
I see the girls walk by dressed in their summer
    clothes
I have to turn my head until my darkness goes

I see a line of cars and they're all painted black
With flowers and my love both never to come back
I see people turn their heads and quickly look away
Like a new born baby it just happens ev'ry day

I look inside myself and see my heart is black
I see my red door and I want it painted black
Maybe then I'll fade away and not have to face the
    facts
It's not easy facing up when your whole world
    is black

No more will my green sea go turn a deeper blue
I could not foresee this thing happening to you
If I look hard enough into the setting sun
My love will laugh with me before the morning
    comes

I see a red door and I want it painted black
No colours anymore I want them to turn black
I see the girls walk by dressed in their summer
    clothes
I have to turn my head until my darkness goes

101

Parachute Woman

Parachute woman land on me tonight
Parachute woman land on me tonight
Well, I'll break big in New Orleans
And I'll overspill in Caroline

Parachute woman join me for a ride
Parachute woman join me for a ride
I'll make my blow in Dallas
And get hot again in half the time

Parachute woman will you blow me out?
Parachute woman will you blow me out?
My heavy throbber's itchin'
Just to lay a solo rhythm down

102

Play With Fire

Well you've got your diamonds
And you've got your pretty clothes
And the chauffeur drives your car
You let ev'rybody know
But don't play with me
'Cause you're playing with fire

Your mother she's an heiress
Owns a block in Saint John's Wood
And your father'd be there with her
If he only could
But don't play with me
'Cause you're playing with fire

Your old man took her diamonds
And tiaras by the score
Now she gets her kicks in Stepney
Not in Knightsbridge anymore
So don't play with me
'Cause you're playing with fire

Now you've got some diamonds
And you will have some others
But you'd better watch your step, girl
Or start living with your mother
So don't play with me
'Cause you're playing with fire

So don't play with me
'Cause you're playing with fire

103

Please Go Home

Well maybe I'm talking too fast
But I won't be the first or the last
In the sea of a thousand you cast
Please go home

I don't have to ask what you do
I just have to look to get you
It means nothing for me to get through
Please go home

I don't want to be on my own
I can't talk much better alone
But I don't have to ring like a phone
Please go home

In some early part of your days
You were told of the devious ways
That you thought you could get without pay
Please go home

You reach a state of your mind
Where it's madness to look and to find
Your false affections though kind
Please go home

104

Respectable

Well now we're respected in society, you ain't
    worried 'bout the things that used to be
We're talking heroin with the President
Yes it's a problem sir, but it can be bent

Well now you're a pillar of society, you're not
    worried about things you used to be
You're a rag trade girl, you're the queen of porn
You're the easiest lay on the White House lawn
Get out of my life – don't come back
Get out of my life – don't come back

She's so respectable, she's so respectable
She's so delectable, she's so respectable
Get out of my life, go take my wife – don't come back
Get out of my life, go take my wife – don't come back

She's so respectable
She's so respectable
She's so respectable
So delectable
Get out of my life, go take my wife – don't come back
Get out of my life, go take my wife – don't come back

She's so respectable
She's so respectable
She's so delectable
She's so respectable

Get out of my life, go take my wife – don't come back
Get out of my life, go take my wife – don't come back
Get out of my life, go take my wife – don't come back

Ride On, Baby

A smile on your face but not in your eyes
You're looking through me
You don't feel it inside
Ride on baby, ride on baby
Ride on baby, ride on baby
I could pick your face in an F.B.I. file
You may look pretty
But I can't say the same for your mind

You walked up to me tryin' to look so shy
But the red round your eye
Shows that you ain't a child
Ride on baby, ride on baby
Ride on baby, ride on baby
I've seen your face in a trashy magazine
You know where you're going
But I don't like the places you've been

Ride on baby, ride on baby
Ride on baby, ride on baby
I can pick your face out from the front or behind
You may've looked pretty
But I can't say the same for your mind

Laugh up a bit more go on give it a try
If I'm not impressed
Well you can still cry
Ride on baby, ride on baby
Ride on baby, ride on baby
By the time you're thirty you'll look sixty five
You won't look pretty
But your friends will have kissed you goodbye

Rip This Joint

Mama says yes
Papa says no
Make up your mind
'Cause I got to go
I'm gonna raise hell at the Union Hall
Drive myself right over the wall
Rip this joint
Gonna save your soul
So round and round and round we go
Roll this joint
Gonna get down low
Start my starter
Gonna stop the show

Oh yeah

Mister President
Mister Immigration Man
Let me in, sweetie
To your fair land
I'm Tampa bound and Memphis too
Short Fat Fanny is on the loose
Dig that sound
On the radio
Then slip it right across into Buffalo
Dick and Pat
In ole D.C.
Well, they're gonna hold
Some grits for me

Oh yeah

Ying yang, you're my thing
Oh, now, baby, won't you hear me sing
Flip flop, fit to drop
Come on, baby, won't you let it rock?

Oh yeah

From San José
Down to Santa Fé
Kiss me quick, baby
Wont'cha make my day
Down to New Orleans with the Dixie Queen
'Cross to Dallas, Texas, with the Butter Queen
Rip this joint
Gonna rip yours too
Some brand new steps and some weight to lose
Gonna roll this joint
Gonna get down low
So round and round and round we'll go
Wham, Bham
Birmingham
Alabam' don't give a damn
Little Rock
Fit to drop
Ah, let it rock

107
Rocks Off

I hear you talking when I'm on the street
Your mouth don't move but I can hear you speak
What's the matter with the boy?
He don't come around no more
Is he checking out for sure?
Is he gonna close the door – on me?

I'm always hearing voices on the street
I want to shout but I can't hardly speak
I was making love last night
To a dancer friend of mine
I can't seem to stay in step
'Cause she comes every time
That she pirouettes – over me

But I only get my rocks off while I'm dreaming
I only get my rocks off while I'm sleeping

I'm zipping through the days
At lightning speed
Plug in, flush out and fight the lucky feed
Heading for the overload
Splattered on the dusty road
Kick me like you've kicked before
I can't even feel the pain no more

But I only get my rocks off while I'm dreaming
I only get my rocks off while I'm sleeping

Feel so hypnotized can't describe the scene
Feel so mesmerized all that inside me
The sunshine bores the daylight out of me
Chasing shadows moonlight mystery

Headed for the overload
Splattered on the dusty road
Kick me like you've kicked before
I can't even feel the pain no more

But I only get my rocks off while I'm dreaming
I only get my rocks off while I'm sleeping

108
Ruby Tuesday

She would never say where she came from
Yesterday don't matter if it's gone
While the sun is bright or in the darkest night
No one knows, she comes and goes
Goodbye Ruby Tuesday
Who could hang a name on you
When you change with ev'ry new day
Still I'm gonna miss you

Don't question why she needs to be so free
She'll tell you it's the only way to be
She just can't be chained to a life where nothing's
    gained
And nothing's lost at such a cost
Goodbye Ruby Tuesday
Who could hang a name on you
When you change with ev'ry new day
Still I'm gonna miss you

There's no time to lose I heard her say
Cash your dreams before they slip away
Dying all the time lose your dreams and you
Will lose your mind ain't life unkind
Goodbye Ruby Tuesday
Who could hang a name on you
When you change with ev'ry new day
Still I'm gonna miss you

Goodbye Ruby Tuesday
Who could hang a name on you
When you change with ev'ry new day
Still I'm gonna miss you

109
Sad Day

Someone woke me up this morning
And I lit a cigarette
Found myself when I stopped yawnin'
Started getting myself dressed
Then I felt I had a dream
I remembered the things that I'd seen
I could still hear the things you said
With that bad dream in my head
It was a sad day bad day sad day bad day

So I called you on the phone
And your friend said 'She's not home'
So I told her where I'd be at
And that you should call me back
Then I looked at the morning mail
I was not even expecting a bill
Your letter started Dear
And it left me with these tears
It was a sad day bad day sad day bad day

Because the times that we had rows
But we patched them up somehow
Because the times I tried to go
But you screamed and told me no
There's only one thing in this world
That I can't understand that's a girl
I keep a-readin' the things you said
Like a bad dream in my head
It was a sad day bad day sad day bad day

Oh what a sad sad old day a sad old day
It was a sad old day a sad old day
It was a bad old day a sad old day a bad old day
If there is one awful thing in this world
That I can't understand that's a girl
It was a sad sad old day sad old day
It was a sad old day

110
(I Can't Get No) Satisfaction

I can't get no satisfaction
I can't get no satisfaction
And I try and I try and I try and I try
I can't get no, I can't get no

When I'm driving in my car
And that man comes on the radio
And he's tellin' me more and more
About some useless information
Supposed to fire my imagination
I can't get no, oh, no, no ,no
Hey, hey, hey, that's what I say

I can't get no satisfaction
I can't get no satisfaction
And I try and I try and I try and I try
I can't get no, I can't get no

When I'm watchin' my T.V.
And that man comes on to tell me
How white my shirts can be
Well, he can't be a man
'Cause he doesn't smoke
The same cigarettes as me
I can't get no, oh, no, no, no
Hey, hey, hey, that's what I say

I can't get no satisfaction
I can't get no girl with action
And I try and I try and I try and I try
I can't get no, I can't get no

When I'm ridin' 'round the world
And I'm doin' this and I'm signin' that
And I'm tryin' to make some girl
Who tells me, baby
Better come back later next week
'Cos you see I'm on a losing streak
I can't get no, oh, no, no, no
Hey, hey, hey, that's what I say

I can't get no, I can't get no
I can't get no satisfaction
No satisfaction, no satisfaction
No satisfaction

Shattered

Shattered, shattered
Love and hope and sex and dreams
Are still surviving on the street
Look at me I'm in tatters
I've been shattered
Shattered

Friends are so alarming
And my lover's never charming
Life's just a cocktail party on the street
Big Apple
People dressed in plastic bags directing traffic
Some kind of fashion (shattered)

Laughter, joy, and loneliness and sex and sex and sex
and sex
Look at me I'm in tatters
I'm shattered
Shattered

All this chitter-chatter, chitter-chatter, chitter-chatter
'bout
Shmatter, Shmatter, Shmatter
I can't give it away on 7th Avenue
This town's been wearing tatters (shattered,
shattered)
Work and work for love and sex
Ain't you hungry for success, success, success,
success
But does it matter (shattered)
Does it matter

Look at me, I'm shattered
I'm shattered
Look at me, I'm shattered

Pride and joy and dreams and sex
That's what makes our town the best
Pride and joy and dirty dreams
Are still surviving on the street
Look at me, I'm shattered
I'm shattered
What does it matter
Does it matter
Does it matter
I'm shattered, shattered

Don't you know the crime rate is going up, up, up, up
To live in this town you must be tough, tough, tough,
tough, tough, tough
You've got rats on the west side
And bed bugs uptown – what a mess this town's in
tatters
I've been shattered

My brain's been battered splattered all over
Manhattan.

This town's full of money grabbers
Go ahead
Bite the Big Apple don't mind the maggots
My brain's been battered
My friends they come around they flatter, flatter,
flatter, flatter, flatter, flatter, flatter
Pile it up, pile it up high on the platter.

112

She Smiled Sweetly

Why do my thoughts loom so large on me
They seem to stay for day after day
And won't disappear, I've tried ev'ry way
But she smiled sweetly, she smiled sweetly
She smiled sweetly and said, 'Don't worry'
Oh no, no, no

Where does she hide it inside of her
That keeps her peace most every day
And won't disappear, my hair's turning grey
But she smiled sweetly, she smiled sweetly
She smiled sweetly and said, 'Don't worry'

There's nothing in why or when
There's no use trying
You're begging again and over again

That's what she said so softly
I understood for once in my life
And feeling good most all of the time
But she smiled sweetly, she smiled sweetly
She smiled sweetly and said, 'Don't worry'
Oh no, no, no
Oh no, no, no
Oh no, no, no

113

She's A Rainbow

She comes in colours ev'rywhere
She combs her hair
She's like a rainbow
Combing colours in the air ev'rywhere
She comes in colours

Have you seen her dressed in blue?
See the sky in front of you
And her face is like a sail
A speck of white so fair and pale
Have you seen a lady fairer?

She comes in colours ev'rywhere
She combs her hair
She's like a rainbow
Combing colours in the air ev'rywhere
She comes in colours

Have you seen her all in gold?
Like a queen in days of old
She shoots colours all around
Like a sunset going down
Have you seen a lady fairer?

She comes in colours ev'rywhere
She combs her hair
She's like a rainbow
Combing colours in the air ev'rywhere
She comes in colours

Shine A Light

Saw you stretched out in Room Ten-O-Nine
With a smile on your face
And a tear right in your eye
Couldn't see to get a line on you
My sweet honey love
Berber jew'lry jangling down the street
Make you shut your eyes at ev'ry woman that
   you meet
Could not seem to get a high on you
My sweet honey love

May the good Lord shine a light on you
Make every song your favourite tune
May the good Lord shine a light on you
Warm like the evening sun

Well, you're drunk in the alley, baby
With your clothes all torn
And your late night friends
Leave you in the cold gray dawn
Just seemed too many flies on you
I just can't brush them off

Angels beating all their wings in time
With smiles on their faces
And a gleam right in their eyes
Thought I heard one sigh for you
Come on up, come on up, now
Come on up, now

May the good Lord shine a light on you
Make every song you sing your favourite tune
May the good Lord shine a light on you
Warm like the evening sun

Short And Curlies

Too bad
She's got you by the boards
You can't get free at all
She's got your name
She's got your number
You're screaming like thunder
And you can't get away at all
It's too bad

She's got you by the boards
You can't break loose at all
She's got your name
She's got your number
You're screaming like thunder
And you're trapped like a rat in a hole
It's too bad

She's got you by the boards
She's nailed you to the wall
Oh it's a shame but it's funny
She's crashed your car
She's spent your money
And you can't get away from it all
It's too bad

She's grabbed a handful
And you can't get away from it all
It's too bad ooh and it's painful
And you can't break away from this
And you can't get away from it all
Too bad

She got you by the boards
She's got your name
She's got your number
You're screaming blue murder
And you can't get away from it all
Too bad

She's got you by the boards she's got you by the
   boards
She's got you by the boards she's got you by the
   boards
Too bad too bad too bad too bad so sad so sad
   too bad too bad too bad . . .

Silver Train

Silver train is a comin', I think I'm gonna get on now
  oh yeah
Silver train is a comin', I think I wanna get on now
  oh yeah

Silver rain is a fallin', fallin' up around my house
  oh yeah
Silver rain is a fallin', fallin' up around my house
  oh yeah oh yeah

And I did not know her name and I did not know
  her name
But I sure liked the way that she laughed and took
  my money
And I did not know her name and I did not know
  her name
But I sure liked the way that she laughed and called
  me honey

Silver rain is a fallin', fallin' up around my house
  oh yeah
Silver bells is a ringin', ringin' up around my house
  ding dong oh yeah

And I did not know her name and I did not know
  her name
But I sure liked the way that she laughed and took
  my money
And I did not know her name and I did not know her
  name
But I sure liked the way that she laughed and called
  me honey

I'm going home on a southbound train with a song in
  my mouth
I'm going home on a southbound train with a song in
  my mouth

Silver train is a runnin', I think I'm gonna get on now
  oh yeah
Silver train is a comin', I think I'm gonna get on now
  oh yeah oh yeah

And I did not know her name and I did not know
  her name
But I sure liked the way that she laughed and took
  my money
And I did not know her name and I did not know
  her name
But I sure liked the way that she laughed and called
  me honey

Silver train is a comin', I think I'm gonna get on now
  oh yeah
Silver train is a comin', I think I'm gonna get on now
  oh yeah oh yeah

Sing This Altogether
(See What Happens)

Why don't we sing this song all together
Open our heads, let the pictures come
And if we close all our eyes together
Then we will see where we all come from

Pictures of us thru the steamy haze
Pictures of us painted on our caves

Why don't we sing this song all together
Open our heads, let the pictures come
And if we close all our eyes together
Then we will see where we all come from

Why don't we sing this song all together
Open our heads, let the pictures come
And if we close all our eyes together
Then we will see where we all come from

Pictures of us beating on our drums
Never stopping till the rain has come

Why don't we sing this song all together
Open our heads, let the pictures come
And if we close all our eyes together
Then we will see where we all come from

Sister Morphine

Sittin' On A Fence

Here I lie in my hospital bed
Tell me, Sister Morphine, when are you comin'
  round again?
Oh! I don't think I could wait that long
Oh, you see that my pain is so strong

All the information stated 'medicine man with
  some pain'
Tell me, Sister Morphine, when are you comin'
  round again?
Oh, I don't think I can wait that long
Oh, you see that I'm not that strong

The scream of the ambulance is soundin' in my ear
Tell me, Sister Morphine, how long have I been
  lyin' here?
What am I doing in this place?
Why does the doctor have no face?
Oh, I can't crawl across the floor
Can't you see, Sister Morphine, I'm just trying
  to score

And that just goes to show things are not what they
  seem
Please, Sister Morphine, turn my nightmare into
  dream
Oh, can't sleep till I'm feeling fine
And that this shot will be in the line

Please, Cousin Cocaine, lay your cool hands on
  my head
Hey, Sister Morphine, you just make her like dead
For you know between the night time and the
  morning of the day
That you sit around and watch and meanwhile the
  sheets stain red

Since I was young I've been very hard to please
And I don't know wrong from right
But there is one thing I will never understand
Some of the sick things that a girl does to a man
So I'm just sittin' on a fence
You can't say I got no sense
Trying to make up my mind
Baby it's so hard to find
So I'm sittin' on a fence

All of my friends at school grew up and settled down
Then they mortgaged up their lives
When things got set too much but I think it's true
They just get married 'cos they've nothing else to do
So I'm just sittin' on a fence
You can't say I got no sense
Trying to make up my mind
Baby it's so hard to find
So I'm sittin' on a fence

The day can come when you get old and sick and
  tired of life
You just never realise
Maybe the choice you made wasn't really right
But you've got her and you don't come back at night
So I'm just sittin' on a fence
You can't say I got no sense
Trying to make up my mind
Baby it's so hard to find
So I'm sittin' on a fence

120

Some Girls

Some girls give me money, some girls buy me clothes
Some girls give me jewellery that I never thought
    I'd own
Some girls give me diamonds, some girls heart
    attacks
Some girls I give all my bread to, I don't ever want
    it back.

Some girls give me jewellery, others buy me clothes
Some girls give me children I never asked them for
So give me all your money, give me all your gold
I'll buy a house back at Zuma Beach and give you
    half of what I owe

Some girls take my money, some girls take my
    clothes
Some girls take the shirt off my back and leave me
    with a lethal dose

French girls they want Cartier, Italian girls want
    cars,
American girls want everything in the world you can
    possibly imagine.
English girls, they're so pretty – I can't stand them on
    the telephone
Sometimes I take the receiver off the hook, I don't
    want them to ever call at all.

White girls they're pretty funny, but sometimes they
    drive me mad
Black girls just want to get fucked all night; I just
    don't have that much jam.

Chinese girls, they're so gentle – they're really such
    a tease
You never know quite what they're cookin' inside
    those silky sleeves.
Give me all your money, give me all your gold
I'll give ya a house back in Zuma Beach and give you
    half of what I owe.

Some girls they're so pure, some girls so corrupt
Some girls give me children I only made love to once
So give me half your money, give me half your car
Give me half of everything – I'll make you the
    world's greatest star by half.
So give me all your money, give me all your gold
Let's go back to Zuma Beach – I'll give you half of
    everything I owe.

121

Some Things Just Stick In Your Mind

Why does the sky turn grey ev'ry night
Sun rise again in time
Why do you think of the first love you had
Some things just stick in your mind

Why does the rain fall down on the earth
Why do the clouds keep cryin'
Why do you sleep curled up like a child
Some things just stick in your mind

Why when the children grow up and leave
Still remember their nursery rhymes
Why must there be so much hate in their lives
Some things just stick in their minds

122

Something Happened To Me Yesterday

Something happened to me yesterday
Something I can't speak of right away
Something happened to me
Something oh so groovy
Something happened to me yesterday

He don't know if it's right or wrong
Maybe he should tell someone
He's not sure just what it was
Or if it's against the law
Something

Something very strange I hear you say
You're talking in a most peculiar way
But something really threw me
Something oh so groovy
Something happened to me yesterday

He don't know just where it's gone
He don't really care at all
No one's sure just what it was
Or the meaning and the cause
Something

He don't know if it's right or wrong
Maybe he should tell someone
He's not sure just what it was
Or if it's against the law
Something

Someone says there's something more to pay
For sins that you committed yesterday
Is really rather drippy
But something oh so trippy
Something happened to me yesterday

He don't know just where it's gone
He don't really care at all
No one's sure just what it was
Or the meaning and the cause
Something

Someone's singing loud across the bay
Sitting on a mat about to pray
Isn't half as loony
As something oh so groovy
Something happened to me yesterday

He don't know if it's right or wrong
Maybe he should tell someone
He's not sure just what it was
Or if it's against the law
Something

123

Soul Survivor

When the waters is rough
The sailing is tough
I'll get drowned in your love
You've got a cut throat crew
I'm gonna sink under you
I got the bell bottom blues
It's gonna be the death of me

It's the graveyard watch
Running right on the rocks
I've taken all of the knocks
You ain't giving me no quarter
I'd rather drink sea water
I wish I'd never had brought you
It's gonna be the death of me

Soul survivor soul survivor
Soul survivor soul survivor
Soul survivor soul survivor
Soul survivor soul survivor
Gonna be the death of me
It's gonna be the death of me

When you're flying your flags
All my confidence sags
You got me packing my bags
I'll stow away at sea
You make me mutiny
Where you are I won't be
You're gonna be the death of me

Soul survivor soul survivor
Soul survivor soul survivor
Soul survivor soul survivor
Soul survivor soul survivor
Gonna be the death of me
It's gonna be the death of me

124

Star Star

Baby, baby, I've been so sad since you've been gone
Way back to New York City where you do belong
Honey, I miss your two-tongued kisses, the legs
    wrapped around me tight
If I ever get back to fun city, girl, I'm gonna make
    you scream all night

Honey, honey, call me on the telephone
I know you are moving out to Hollywood with your
    can of tasty foam
All those beat up friends of mine got to get them in
    my book
And lead guitars and movie stars get their toes
    beneath my hook
Yeah you were starbucker starbucker star
Starbucker starbucker star
Starbucker starbucker star

Yes I heard about your polaroids now that's what I
    call obscene
Your tricks with fruit were kinda cute now that really
    is a scene
Honey, I miss your two-tongued kisses legs wrapped
    around me tight
If I ever get back to New York I'm gonna make you
    scream all night
Yeah you were starbucker starbucker star
Starbucker starbucker star
Starbucker starbucker star

At the party I got mad at you for giving it to
    Steve McQueen
And you and me made a pretty pair falling through
    the silver screen
Now, Baby, I am open to anything I don't know
    where to draw the line
Well I'm making bets that you gonna get your man
    before he dies
You were starbucker starbucker starbucker star
Were starbucker starbucker starbucker star
Were starbucker starbucker starbucker star
Were starbucker starbucker starbucker star

125

Stoned

Instrumental

126
Stop Breaking Down

Everytime I'm walking
All down the street
Some pretty mama
Start breaking down on me
Stop breaking down
Baby, please, stop breaking down
Stuff is gonna bust your brains out, baby
Gonna make you lose your mind

You Saturday night women now
You just ape and clown
You don't do nothing
But tear my reputation down
Stop breaking down
Momma, please, stop breaking down
Stuff is gonna bust your brains out, baby
Yeah, it's gonna make you lose your mind

I love my baby
Ninety nine degrees
But that momma got a pistol
Laid it down on me
Stop breaking down
Baby, please, stop breaking down
Stuff is gonna bust your brains out, baby
Yeah, gonna make you lose your mind

Everytime I'm walking
All down the street
Some pretty woman
Start breaking down on me
Stop breaking down
Mama, please, stop breaking down
Stuff is gonna bust your brains out, baby
Gonna make you lose your mind

127
Stray Cat Blues

I hear the click-clack of your feet on the stairs
I know you're scare-eyed honey
There'll be a feast if you just come upstairs
But it's no hanging matter, it's no capital crime

I can see that you're fifteen years old
No, I don't want your I.D.
You look so restless and so far from home
But it's no hanging matter, it's no capital crime

Oh yeah, you're a strange stray cat
Oh yeah, don't scratch like that
Oh yeah, you're a strange stray cat
But your mama don't know you scream like that
Bet she don't know that you spit like that

You look so weird and you're so far from home
But you really miss your mother
Don't look so scared, I'm no mad-brained bear
But it's no hanging matter, it's no capital crime

Oh yeah, you're a strange stray cat
Oh yeah, don't scream like that
Bet your mama don't know you scratch like that
Bet she don't know you can bite like that

You say you got a friend, she's wilder than you
Well, why don't you bring her upstairs
If she's so wild, well she can join in too
But it's no hanging matter, it's no capital crime

Oh yeah, you're a strange stray cat
Oh yeah, don't scratch like that
Oh yeah, you're a strange stray cat
Bet your mama don't know you bite like that
I bet she never saw you scratch my back

128

Street Fighting Man

Ev'rywhere I hear the sound of marching, charging
  feet, oh, boy
'Cause summer's here and the time is right for
  fighting in the street, oh, boy
But what can a poor boy do
Except to sing for a rock 'n' roll band
'Cause in sleepy London town
There's just no place for street fighting man
No

Hey! Think the time is right for a palace revolution
But where I live the game to play is compromise
  solution
Well, then what can a poor boy do
Except to sing for a rock 'n' roll band
'Cause in sleepy London town
There's just no place for street fighting man
No

Hey! Said my name is called disturbance
I'll shout and scream, I'll kill the king, I'll rail at all
  his servants
Well, what can a poor boy do
Except to sing for a rock 'n' roll band
'Cause in sleepy London town
There's just no place for street fighting man
No

129

Stupid Girl

I'm not talking about the kind of clothes she wears
Look at that stupid girl
I'm not talking about the way she combs her hair
Look at that stupid girl
The way she powders her nose
Her vanity shows and it shows
She's the worst thing in this world
Well look at that stupid girl

I'm not talking about the way she digs for gold
Look at that stupid girl
Well I'm talking about the way she grabs and holds
Look at that stupid girl
The way she talks about someone else
That she don't even know herself
She the sickest thing in this world
Look at that stupid girl

Well I'm sick and tired
And I really have my doubts
I've tried and tried
But it never really works out
Like a lady in waiting to a virgin queen
Look at that stupid girl
She bitches about things that she's never seen
Look at that stupid girl
It doesn't matter if she dyes her hair
Or the colour of the shoes she wears
She's the worst thing in this world
Look at that stupid girl

Like a lady in waiting to a virgin queen
Look at that stupid girl
She bitches about things that she's never seen
Look at that stupid girl
She purrs like a pussy cat
Then she turns round and hisses back
She's the sickest thing in this world
Look at that stupid girl

130
Surprise Surprise

Heard from friends o' mine
You've bin tellin' lies
How I was wrapt up in you
But surprise surprise
Surprise surprise
I never wanted you that bad
'Cos I knew you was tellin' lies
Knew you was tellin' lies
I could see it in your eyes

Why did you have to
Go and fool after
We had got along so fine
But surprise surprise
Surprise surprise
Ain't nothin' strange to me
'Cos I knew you was tellin' lies
Knew you was tellin' lies
I could see it in your eyes

I hope you're tired of
All your chasin' round
Thinkin' I'm alone all night
But surprise surprise
Surprise surprise
You're only fooling yourself
Knew you was tellin' lies
I could see it in your eyes

131
Sway

Did you ever wake up to find
A day that broke up your mind
Destroyed your notions of circular time

It's just that demon life that got you in its sway
It's just that demon life that got you in its sway

Ain't flinging tears out on the dusty ground
For my friends up on the dusty ground
Can't stand the feeling getting so brought down

It's just that demon life that got you in its sway
It's just that demon life that got you in its sway

There must be ways to find out
Love is the way they say is really strutting out

One day I woke up to find
Right in the bed next to mine
Someone who broke me up with a corner of her smile

It's just that demon life that got you in its sway
It's just that demon life that got you in its sway

Sweet Black Angel

Sweet Virginia

Got a sweet black angel
Got a pin up girl
Got a sweet black angel
Up upon my wall
Well she ain't no singer
And she ain't no star
But she sure talk good
But she move so fast
But de girl in danger
Yeah de girl in chains
But she keep on pushin'
Would ya take her place?
She countin' up de minutes
She countin' up de days
She's a sweet black angel
Not a sweet black slave

Ten little niggers
Sittin' on a wall
Her brothers been a' fallin'
Fallin' one by one
For a judge's murder
In a judge's court
Now de judge gonna judge her
For all dat he's worth
Well de gal in danger
De gal in chains
But she keeps on pushin'
Would you do the same?
She countin' up de minutes
She countin' up de days
She's a sweet black angel
Not a gun toting teacher
Not a Red lovin' school mom
Ain't someone gonna free her
Free de sweet black slave
Free de sweet black slave
Free de sweet black slave

Wading through the waste stormy winter
And there's not a friend to help you through
Trying to stop the waves behind your eyeballs
Drop your reds drop your greens and blues

Thank you for your wine, California
Thank you for your sweet and bitter fruits
Yes, I've got the desert in my toenail
And hid the speed inside my shoe

But come on come on down Sweet Virginia
Come on honey child I beg of you
Come on come on down you got it in you
Got to scrape that shit right off your shoes

Sympathy For The Devil

Please allow me to introduce myself
I'm a man of wealth and taste
I've been around for many a long, long year
I've stolen many a man's soul and faith
I was around when Jesus Christ had His moments of
    doubt and pain
I made damn sure that Pilate washed his hands and
    sealed his fate

Pleased to meet you, hope you guess my name
But what's puzzling you, is the nature of my game

I stuck around St. Petersburg
When I saw it was time for a change
I killed the Tzar and his ministers
Anastasia screamed in vain
I rode a tank, held a gen'ral's rank
When the blitzkrieg raged and the bodies stank

Pleased to meet you, hope you guess my name
But what's puzzling you, is the nature of my game

I watched with glee while your kings and queens
Fought for ten decades for the gods they made
I shouted out, 'Who killed the Kennedys?'
When after all it was you and me

So let me please introduce myself
I am a man of wealth and taste
And I lay traps for troubadours
Who get killed before they reach Bombay

Pleased to meet you, hope you guess my name
But what's puzzling you, is the nature of my game

Just as every cop is criminal
And all the sinners, Saints
As heads is tails, just call me Lucifer
'Cause I'm in need of some restraint
So if you meet me, have some courtesy
Have some sympathy and some taste
Use all your well-learned politesse
Or I'll lay your soul to waste

Pleased to meet you, hope you guess my name
But what's puzzling you, is the nature of my game

2,000 Light Years From Home

Sun turning round with graceful motion
We're setting off with soft explosion
Bound for a star with fiery oceans

It's so very lonely
You're a hundred light years from home

Freezing red deserts turn to dark
Energy's here in ev'ry part

It's so very lonely
You're six hundred light years from home

It's so very lonely
You're a thousand light years from home

It's so very lonely
You're a thousand light years from home

Bill flight fourteen you now can land
See you on Alder Boran
Safe on the green desert sand

It's so very lonely
You're two thousand light years from home

It's so very lonely
You're two thousand light years from home

136
2,000 Man

Well, my name is a number, a piece of plastic film
And I grow tiny flow'rs in my little window sill
Don't you know I'm the two thousand man?
And my kids, they just don't understand me at all

Tho' my wife still respects me, I really misuse her
I am having an affair with a random computer
Don't you know I'm the two thousand man?
And my kids, they just don't understand me at all

Oh, daddy, be proud of your planet
Oh, mummy, be proud of your sun
Oh, daddy, be proud of your planet
Oh, mummy, be proud of your sun

Oh, daddy, is your brain still flashing
Like it did when you were young?
Or did you come down crashing
Seeing all the things you done?
Oh, it's a big put-on

Oh, daddy, be proud of your planet
Oh, mummy, be proud of your sun
Oh, daddy, be proud of your planet
Oh, mummy, be proud of your sun
And you know who's the two thousand man
And your kids they just won't understand you at all

137
2120 South Michigan Avenue

Instrumental

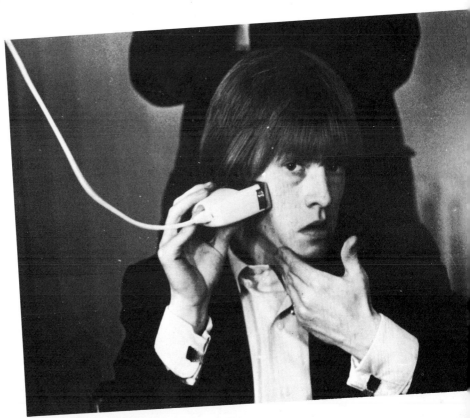

Take It Or Leave It

You can turn off and on more times
Than a flashing neon sign when you want
You're bad, but you can be so kind
Just take it, or leave it
Don't tell your friends
Just what you're gonna do now
You take it, or leave it is just my line

There've been times when you try making eyes
At all my so called friends then you go
Now you're back, but you can be so kind
Just take it, or leave it
Don't tell your friends
Just what you're gonna do now
You take it, or leave it is just my line
Lalalalalalalalalalalalalalalalalalalalalala
Lalalalalalalalalalalalalalalalalalalalalala

I'm sick and tired of the smile that you give
When you don't come home at night you said you'd
    called
That's a lie, but you can be so kind
Just take it, or leave it
Don't tell your friends
Just what you're gonna do now
You take it, or leave it is just my line
Lalalalalalalalalalalalalalalalalalalalalala
Lalalalalalalalalalalalalalalalalalalalalala

Tell Me

I want you back again I want your love again
I know you find it hard to reason with me
But this time it's different darling you'll see
You gotta tell me you're coming back to me
You gotta tell me you're coming back to me
You gotta tell me you're coming back to me
You gotta tell me you're coming back to me

You said we're through before you walked out on me
    before
I tried to tell you but you didn't want to know
This time you're different and determined to go
You gotta tell me you're coming back to me
You gotta tell me you're coming back to me
You gotta tell me you're coming back to me
You gotta tell me you're coming back to me

I wait as the days go by I long for the nights to go by
I hear the knock on my door that never comes
I hear the telephone that hasn't rung
You gotta tell me you're coming back to me
You gotta tell me you're coming back to me
You gotta tell me you're coming back to me
You gotta tell me you're coming back to me

140

The Lantern

We, in our present life
Knew that the stars were right
So, if you are the first to go
You'll leave a sign to let me know
Oh, tell me so
Please, carry the lantern high

You cross the sea of night
Free from the spell of flight
Your cloak it is a spirit shroud
Wake me in my sleeping hours
Like a cloud
Please, carry the lantern high

Me, in my sorry plight
You waiting ev'ry night
My face, it turns a deathly pale
You're talking to me through your veil
I hear you wail
Please, carry the lantern high

The servants sleep
The door is barred
You hear the stopping of my heart
Please, carry the lantern high

141

(This Could Be)
The Last Time

I've told you once and I've told you twice
You'd better listen to my advice
You don't try very hard to please me
With what you know it should be easy

Well this could be the last time
This could be the last time
Maybe the last time
I don't know
Oh no

I'm sorry girl but I can't stay
Feeling like I do to-day
Staying here is too much sorrow
Guess I'll feel the same tomorrow

Well this could be the last time
This could be the last time
Maybe the last time
I don't know
Oh no

Well this could be the last time
This could be the last time
Maybe the last time
I don't know
Oh no

I've told you once and I've told you twice
Someone'll have to pay the price
Here's the chance to change your mind
I'll be gone a long long time

Well this could be the last time
This could be the last time
Maybe the last time
I don't know
Oh no

142

The Salt Of The Earth

Let's drink to the hard working people
Let's drink to the lowly of birth
Raise your glass to the good and the evil
Let's drink to the salt of the earth

Say a pray'r for the commonfoot soldier
Spare a thought for this back-breaking work
Say a pray'r for his wife and his children
Who burn the fires and who still till the earth

And when I search a faceless crowd
A swirling mass of gray and black and white
They don't look real to me
In fact they look so strange

Raise your glass to the hard working people
Let's drink to the uncounted heads
Let's think of the wavering millions
Who need leaders but get gamblers instead

Spare a thought for the stay-at-home voter
His empty eyes gaze at strange beauty shows
And a parade of gray suited grafters
A choice of cancer or polio

And when I search a faceless crowd
A swirling mass of gray and black and white
They don't look real to me
In fact they look so strange

Let's drink to the hard working people
Let's drink to the lowly of birth
Spare a thought for the ragtaggy people
Let's drink to the salt of the earth

Let's drink to the hard working people
Let's drink to the salt of the earth
Let's think of the two thousand million
Let's think of the humble of birth

143

The Singer, Not The Song

Ev'rywhere you want I always go
I always give in because, baby, you know
You just say so 'cause you give me that feeling inside
That I know I must be right
It's the singer not the song

It's not the way you give in willingly
Others do it without thrilling me
Giving me that same old feeling inside
That I know I must be right
It's the singer not the song

The same old places and the same old songs
We've been going there for much too long
There's something wrong and it gives me that feeling
   inside
That I know must be right
It's the singer not the song

144

The Spider And The Fly

Sittin' thinkin' sinkin' drinkin'
Wond'ring what I'll do when I'm through tonight
Smokin' mopin' maybe just hopin'
Some little girl will pass on by
To wanna be alone
But I love my girl at home
I remember what she said
She said, My! My! My!
Don't tell lies!
Keep fidelity in your head!
My! My! My! Don't tell lies
When you've done your show go to bed
Don't say Hi! like a spider to a fly
Jump right ahead and you're dead!

Sit up fed up low down go 'round
Down to the bar at the place I'm at
Sittin' drinkin' superficially thinkin'
About the rins'd out blonde on my left
And then I said Hi! like a spider to a fly
Rememb'ring what my little girl said
She was coming flirty
She look'd about thirty
I would have run away, but I was on my own
She told me later she's a machine operator
She said she liked the way I held the microphone
I said My! My! like a spider to a fly
Jump right ahead in my web!

145

The Under Assistant West Coast Promotion Man

Well I'm waiting at the bus stop heading down town
    L.A.
Well I'm waiting at the bus stop heading down town
    L.A.
Well I'd much rather be on a bird-walk on Broadway

Well I'm sitting here thinking just how sharp I am
Well I'm sitting here thinking just how sharp I am
I'm an under assistant west coast promo man

Well I promo groups when they come into town
Well I promo groups when they come into town
Well they laugh at my toupé, they sure put me down

Well I'm sitting here thinking just how sharp I am
Well I'm sitting here thinking just how sharp I am
I'm a necessary talent behind ev'ry rock 'n' roll band

Think

Through The Lonely Nights

I'm giving you a piece of my mind
There's no charge of any kind
Try again a simple test
You shouldn't trust that time will trace your steps
So think back back a little bit baby
Back back well it's all right
You gotta think think a bit about it baby
Think think a bit about it baby
Think think a bit about it baby
Tell me whose fault was that then?
Tell me whose fault was that then?

Think about a year ago
How we lived I'll never know
Conning people for a small dime
Here's another piece of my mind
So think back back a little bit baby
Back back well it's all right
You gotta think think a bit about it baby
Think think a bit about it baby
Think think a bit about it baby
Tell me whose fault was that then?
Tell me whose fault was that then?

Changes may have come too fast
But I thought we'll always last
Situations may have changed
But I think we're still the same
So think back back a little bit baby
Back back well it's all right
You gotta think think a bit about it baby
Think think a bit about it baby
Think think a bit about it baby
Tell me whose fault was that then?
Tell me whose fault was that then?

We're not children any more
We don't need to play with toys
Take a look and you will surely find
You're getting much too old before your time
So think back back a little bit baby
Back back well it's all right
You gotta think think a bit about it baby
Think think a bit about it baby
Think think a bit about it baby
Tell me whose fault was that then?
Tell me whose fault was that then?

Through the lonely nights
I think of you
Through the lonely hours
I dream of you
I don't know why I do it but I do
Why do you take it what's wrong with you?
Ev'ry time I see ya
Ev'ry time I see ya
Ev'ry time I see you
With the lonely weekends I'm far from you
Why you're coming on, like you're supposed to do?
Oh but you know me so well
And your time ain't so hard to sell
In your cherry dresses and your shiny shoes
In a doorway on some neon walk
Making the lonely pay for me
Why don't we set each other free
When did I mislead ya
When did I mistreat ya
When did I mistreat ya
When did I deceive ya

Till The Next Goodbye

Honey, is there any place that you would like to be
I know a Coffeeshop down on Fifty second street
And I don't need no fancy food and I don't need no
    fancy wine
And I sure don't need the tears you cry

Till the next time we say goodbye
Till the next time we say goodbye
Till the next time we say goodbye
I'll be thinking of you
I'll be thinking of you

A movie house on Forty second street
Ain't a very likely place for you and I to meet
Watching the snow swirl around your hair and
    around your feet
And I'm thinking to myself you surely look a treat

Till the next time we say goodbye
Till the next time we say goodbye
Till the next time we say goodbye
I'll be thinking of you
I'll be thinking of you

I can't go on like this, can you?
You give me a cure all from New Orleans
Now that's a recipe I sure do need
Some cider vinegar and some elderberry wine
May cure all your ills, but it can't cure mine
Your Louisiana recipes have let me down
Your Louisiana recipes have surely let me down

Till the next time we say goodbye
Till the next time we say goodbye
Till the next time we say goodbye
I'll be thinking of you
I'll be thinking of you

Time Waits For No One

Yes star crossed in pleasure
The stream flows on by
Yes as we are sated in leisure
We watch it fly
And time waits for no one
And it won't wait for me
Time waits for no one
And it won't wait for me

Time can tear down a building
Or destroy a woman's face
Hours are like diamonds
Don't let them waste

Time waits for no one
No favours has he
Time waits for no one
And it won't wait for me

La la la

Time waits for no one
And it won't wait for me
Time waits for no man
And it won't wait for you

Men they build towers to their passing
To their fame everlasting
Here he comes chopping and reaping
Hear him laugh at their cheating

Time waits for no man
And it won't wait for me
Yes time waits for no one
And it won't wait for me

Drink in your summer
Gather your corn
The dreams of the night-time
Will vanish by dawn
And time waits for no one

And it won't wait for me
Time waits for no one
And it won't wait for me

No, no, no, not for me
No, not for me . . .

Torn And Frayed

Try A Little Harder

Hey, let him follow you down
Way under ground
Wind and he's bound
Bound to follow you down
Just a dead beat
Right off the street
Bound to follow you down

Well the ballrooms and smelly bordellos
And dressing rooms filled with parasites
On stage the band has got problems
They're a bag of nerves on first nights
He ain't tied down to no home town
Yeah, and he thought he was reckless
You think he's bad
He thinks you're mad
Yeah, and the guitar player gets restless

Well his coat is torn and frayed
It's seen much better days
Just as long as the guitar plays
Let it steal your heart away

Joe's got a cough
Sounds kinda rough
Yeah, and the codeine to fix it
Doctor prescribes
Drugstore supplies
Who's gonna help him to kick it?

Well his coat is torn and frayed
It's seen much better days
Just as long as the guitar plays
Let it steal your heart away

Don't you worry try a little harder
Don't you worry try a little harder
Don't you worry try a little harder
Don't you worry try a little harder
The girl really wants you man, don't you see
You gotta give her all the lovin' that she needs
Gotta try, try it one more time
Just try, try it one more time

Don't you worry try a little harder
Don't you worry try a little harder
Give her lovin' that's a little stronger
Give her lovin' that's a little stronger
If you want your baby when the day turns to night
You gotta give her lovin' make her feel alright
'S alright, it's alright
Try it one more time it's alright

Don't you worry try a little harder
Don't you worry try a little harder
Say goodnight and stay a little longer
Say goodnight and stay a little longer
You have to keep her from cryin' you got to try
To work pretty hard to keep her satisfied
Just try, try it one more time
Try it, gotta try, try a little bit harder . . .

152
Tumbling Dice

Women think I'm tasty
But they're always tryin' to waste me
And make me burn the candle right down
But baby, baby, I don't need no jewels in my crown
'Cause all you women is low down gamblers
Cheatin' like I don't know how
But baby, baby, there's fever in the funk house now

This low down bitchin' got my poor feet a-itchin'
You know, you know the deuce is still wild
Baby, I can't stay
You got to roll me and call me the tumblin' dice

Always in a hurry
I never stop to worry
Don't you see the time flashin' by
Honey, got no money
I'm all sixes and sevens and nines
Say now, baby, I'm the rank outsider
You can be my partner in crime
But, baby, I can't stay
You got to roll me and call me the tumblin'
Roll me and call me the tumblin' dice

Oh, my, my, my, I'm the lone crap shooter
Playin' the field ev'ry night
Baby, can't stay
You got to roll me and call me the tumblin'
Roll me and call me the tumblin' dice

153
Turd On The Run

Grabbed hold of your coat tail but it come off in my
hand
I reached for your lapel, but it weren't sewn on so
grand
Begged, promised anything if only you would stay
Well, I lost a lot of love over you

Fell down to my knees and I hung on to your pants
But you just kept on runnin' while they ripped off in
my hands
Di'mond rings, vaseline, you give me disease
Well, I lost a lot of love over you

I boogied in the ballroom I boogied in the dark
Tie your hands, tie your feet, throw you to the sharks
Make you sweat, make you scream, make you wish
you'd never been
I lost a lot of love over you

Under My Thumb

Under my thumb's the girl who once had me down
Under my thumb's the girl who once pushed me
  around
It's down to me, the diff'rence in the clothes she
  wears
It's down to me, the change has come, she's under
  my thumb

Under my thumb's a squirming dog who's just had
  her day
Under my thumb's a girl who has just changed her
  ways
It's down to me, the way she does just what she's told
It's down to me, the change has come, she's under
  my thumb

Under my thumb's a siamese cat of a girl
Under my thumb she's the sweetest pet in the world
It's down to me, she does just what she's told
It's down to me, the change has come, she's under
  my thumb

Under my thumb her eyes are just kept to herself
Under my thumb well I can still look at someone else
It's down to me, the way she talks when she's spoken
  to
It's down to me, the change has come, she's under
  my thumb

Ventilator Blues

When your spine is cracking and your hands they
  shake
Heart is bursting and your butt's gonna break
Your woman's cussing you can hear her scream
You feel like murder in the first degree
Ain't nobody slowing down no way
Everybody's stepping on their accelerator
Don't matter where you are
Everybody's gonna need a ventilator

When you're trapped and circled with no second
  chances
Your code of living is your gun in hand
We can't be browed by beating, we can't be cowed
  by words
Messed by cheating, ain't gonna ever learn
Everybody walking around
Everybody trying to step on their Creator
Don't matter where you are
Everybody, everybody gonna need
Some kind of ventilator
Some kind of ventilator
What you gonna do about it
What you gonna do?
What you gonna do about it
What you gonna do?
Gonna fight it?
Gonna fight it?
Gonna fight it?

(Walking Thru The) Sleepy City

Walkin' thru' the sleepy city
In the night it looks so pretty
Till I got to that one café
That stays open night and day

When you walk thru' the sleepy city
In the night it looks so pretty
Till I got to that one café
That stays open night and day

That's where I'm gonna listen
To what people say
They just sit 'n' hear the radio play
No one sees me on my own
Guess I'll just be sleepy
In my sleepy city

We Love You

We don't care if you'd only love we
We don't care if you'd only love we

We love you
We love you
And we hope that you will love we too
We love they
We love they
And we want you to love they too

We don't care if you hound we
And lock the doors around we
We've locked it in our minds
'Cos we love you
We love you

You will never love we
The uniforms don't fit we
You're dead 'n' then we're in
'Cos we love you
We love you
Of course we do

I love you
I love you
And I hope that you are grooving too
We love you we do

158

We're Wasting Time

We're wasting time inside my mind
The thought of you won't go away come every day
We're just wasting time

We're wasting time
My clothes are fine
Still fresh and clean
The sweet perfume in our balloon
We're just wasting time

With that face that I've seen
Maybe thinks the same as me
Well there is nothing that we're learning
While her hands keep turning
Oh girl! Oh girl! Can't you see

Wasting time inside my mind
The thought of you won't go away come every day
We're just wasting time

We're wasting time
My clothes are fine
Still fresh and clean
The sweet perfume in our balloon
We're just wasting time

159

What A Shame

What a shame nothing seems to be going right
What a shame nothing seems to be going right
It seems easy to me that ev'rything could be all right

What a shame they always wanna start a fight
What a shame they always wanna start a fight
Well it scares me so I have to sleep in a shelter all
    night

What a shame y'all heard what I said
What a shame y'all heard what I said
You might wake up in the morning find you poor
    selves dead

What To Do

What to do, yeah, I really don't know
I really don't know what to do
What to do, yeah, I really don't know
I really don't know

Maybe when the T.V. stops
Fading out on the epilogue
Watch the screen just fade away
No, I really don't know
I really don't know what to do yeah
Well I really don't know
I really don't know what to do
What to do yeah I really don't know
I really don't know

There's a place where you get bored
That's what you make your money for
Drink and dance till four o'clock
Now you really don't know
You really don't know what to do yeah
There's nothing to do
And nowhere to go
You're talking to people
That you don't know
There's na-na-nothing to do do do
There's na-na-nothing no
You really don't know what to do yeah
Well I really don't know
I really don't know what to do
What to do yeah, I really don't know
I really don't know

Hurry people get on your train
Don't be late for work again
I think it's time to go to bed
No I really don't know
I really don't know what to do yeah
There's nothing to do
And nowhere to go
You're talking to people
That you don't know
There's na-na-nothing to do do do
There's na-na-nothing no
You really don't know what to do

When The Whip Comes Down

Momma and Poppa told me I was crazy to stay
I'd be gay in New York I was a fag in L.A.
So I saved my money and I took a plane
But wherever I go they treat me the same.

But when the whip comes down
When the whip comes down
When the whip comes down
When the whip comes down

I go to 53rd Street and they spit in my face
But I'm learning the ropes yeh I'm learning the trade
The east river truckers are churning with trash
I got so much money but I spend it so fast.

When the whip comes down
When the whip comes down
When the whip comes down
When the whip comes down
When the shit hits the fan
I'll be sitting on the can
When the whip comes down

Some call me garbage when I'm sweeping up the
    street
But I never roll and I ain't never cheat
I'm filling the need
Yeh I'm plugging the hole
My Momma's so glad that I ain't on the dole

When the whip comes down
When the whip comes down
When the shit hits the fan
I'll be sitting on the can
When the whip comes down
When the whip comes down

When the whip comes down
When the whip comes down
When the whip comes down
I'll be running this town
When the whip comes down
Watch out baby

When the whip comes down
When the whip comes down
I'll be running this town
When the shit hits the fan
I'll be sitting on the can
When the whip comes down
Check it out, check it out, check it out, check it out . .

Who's Been Sleeping Here

Who's Driving Your Plane

What d'you say, girl, you say what is wrong
You must be joking, you was led along
But the butler, the baker, the laughing cavalier
Will tell me now who's been sleeping here

What d'you say girl, who'd you see that night?
Oh I was doing something right
But the soldier, the sailor, and then there's the three
 musketeers
They'll tell me now, who's been sleeping here

Don't you look like, like a Goldilocks?
There must be somewhere, somewhere you can stop
There's the noseless old newsboy, the old British
 brigadier
They'll tell me now who's been sleeping here

Who's been eating, eating off my plate?
Who will tell me, who'll investigate?
There's the sergeants, the soldiers, the cruel old
 grenadiers
They'll tell me now, who's been sleeping here

It was your father who trained you
And your mother who brained you
To be so useless and shy
But I just replaced them
And tried not to break them
Because you could stand up if you try
And I wanna see your face
When your knees and your legs
Just gonna break down and die
Who's driving your plane?
Who's driving your plane?
Who's driving your plane?
Who's driving your plane?
Are you in control or
Is it driving you insane?

If I could wave a magic wand
Then maybe you'd change back
To being a blonde
And your skirt would come down
And cover your feet
If I said it's not camp
To wear a Tiffany lamp
You'd throw it right out in the street
Who's driving your plane?
Who's driving your plane?
Who's driving your plane?
Who's driving your plane?
Are you in control or
Is it driving you insane?

You could stand on your head
Or maybe sing in your bed
If I said it was the thing to do
If you're in with the faces
And their getaway places
But they don't take no notice of you
Well those trendy pace setters
Will just cause you the pain
'Cause they will wanna know
Who's driving your plane?

Wild Horses

Winter

Childhood living is easy to do
The things you wanted I bought them for you
Graceless lady you know who I am
You know I can't let you slide through my hands

Wild horses couldn't drag me away,
Wild, wild horses, couldn't drag me away

I watched you suffer a dull aching pain,
Now you've decided to show me the same
No sweeping exits or offstage lines
Could make me feel bitter or treat you unkind

Wild horses couldn't drag me away,
Wild, wild horses, couldn't drag me away

I know I've dreamed you a sin and a lie,
I have my freedom but I don't have much time
Faith has been broken, tears must be cried,
Let's do some living after we die

Wild horses couldn't drag me away,
Wild, wild horses, we'll ride them some day

Wild horses couldn't drag me away,
Wild, wild horses, we'll ride them some day

And it sure has been a cold cold winter
And the wind it ain't been blowing from the south
And it sure has been a cold cold winter
And the light of love is all burned out
And it sure has been a hard hard winter
And my feet been draggin' 'cross the ground
And I hope it's gonna be a long hot summer
And the light of love will be burning bright
And I wish I'd been out in California
When the lights on all the Christmas trees went out
But I been burning my bell book and candle
And the restoration plays have all gone round

And it sure has been a cold cold winter
My feet been draggin' 'cross the ground
And the fields has all been brown and barren
And the springtime takes a long way around
And I wish I'd been out in Stony Canyon
When the lights on all the Christmas trees went out
But I been burning my bell book and candle
And the restoration plays have all gone round

Oh Lord well well well
Sometimes I think about you baby
Sometimes I cry about you Lord yeah
And I'll wrap my coat around you
Sometimes I wanna keep you warm baby
Sometimes I wanna burn a candle for you

A...
After the pa...
After all this what ha... ...ieved?
I've realised it's time to leave

'Cause who wants yesterday's papers?
Who wants yesterday's girl?
Who wants yesterday's papers
Nobody in the world

Living a life of constant change
Every day means a turn of a page
Yesterday's papers are such bad news
The same thing applies to me and you

Who wants yesterday's papers?
Who wants yesterday's girl?
Who wants yesterday's papers?
Nobody in the world

Seems very hard to have just one girl
When there's a million in the world
All of these people just can't wait
To fall right into their big mistake

'Cause who wants yesterday's papers?
Who wants yesterday's girl?
Who wants yesterday's papers?
Nobody in the world

167

You Can't Always Get What You Want

I saw her today at the reception
A glass of wine in her hand
I knew she would meet her connection
At her feet was her footloose man
You can't always get what you want
You can't always get what you want
You can't always get what you want
But if you try sometimes
You just might find
You get what you need

And I went down to the demonstration
To get my fair share of abuse
Singing, 'We're gonna vent our frustration
If we don't we're gonna blow a fifty amp fuse'
You can't always get what you want
You can't always get what you want
You can't always get what you want
But if you try sometimes
You just might find
You get what you need

I went down to the Chelsea drugstore
To get your prescription filled
I was standing in line with Mister Jimmy
(And man, did he look pretty ill!)
We decided that we would have a soda
My fav'rite flavour, cherry red
I sang my song to Mister Jimmy
And he said one word to me and that was 'Dead'
You can't always get what you want
You can't always get what you want
You can't always get what you want
But if you try sometimes
You just might find
You get what you need

I saw her today at the reception
In her glass was a bleeding man
She was practised at the art of deception
I could tell by her bloodstained hands
You can't always get what you want
You can't always get what you want
You can't always get what you want
But if you try sometimes
You just might find
You get what you need

168
You Got The Silver

Hey babe, what's in your eyes?
I saw them flashing like airplane lights
You fill my cup, babe, that's for sure
But I must come back for a little more

You got my heart, you got my soul
You got the silver, you got the gold
You got the diamonds from the mines
And that's allright it'll buy some time

Tell me honey what will I do
When I am hungry and thirsty too
Feeling foolish (and that's for sure!)
Just waiting here at your kitchen door?

Hey baby, what's in your eyes?
Is that the diamonds from the mines?
What's that laughing in your smile?
I don't care, no, I don't care

Oh, baby, you got the soul
You got the silver, you got the gold
A flash of love just made me blind
I don't care, no, that's no big surprise

169
You Gotta Move

You gotta move
You gotta move child
You gotta move

Oh when the Lord gets ready
You gotta move
You gotta move
You gotta move child
You gotta move

You may be high
You may be low
You may be rich child or maybe poor
But when the Lord gets ready
You gotta move
Ah ah ah ah ha ha ha ha ha
You gotta move

Ha ah ha ha, Ha ha ha
ha ha ha ha ha ha ha ha ha
Ah ha ha ha ha
ha ha ha ha ha you gotta move.

You see that woman who walks the street
You see that policeman upon his beat
But when the Lord gets ready
You gotta move
Ah ha ha.

Ha ah ha ha ha
Ha ha ha ha ha ha ha ha ha ha ha ha
Ah ha ha ha ha ha ha ha ha
You gotta move.

170

Cocksucker Blues

Well, I'm a lonesome schoolboy and I just came
    into town
Yeah, I'm a lonesome schoolboy and I just came
    into town
Well, I heard so much about London I decided to
    check it out

Well, I wait in Leicester Square where the guy never
    looks in my eye
Yeah, I'm leanin' on Nelsons Column but all I do
    is talk to the lime

Oh where can I get my cock sucked, where can I
    get my arse fucked
I ain't got no money, but I know where to put it
    every time

Well, I asked a young policeman if he'd only
    lock me up for the night
Well, I've had pigs in the farmyard – some of them,
    some of them are alright,
Well, he fucked me with his truncheon and his helmet
    was way too tight

171

Dance

Hey, what am I doing, standing here on the corner of
West 8th Street and 6th Avenue,
And you're asking me nothing.
Keith,
What you doing. Ah.
I think the time has come to get up and get out

Get up, get out
Yeah, into something new
Get up, get out
Into something new

Ooh and it's got me moving

My my my

Poor man eyes the rich man
And denigrates his poverty
The rich man eyes the poor man
And envies his simplicity

Get up get out

Ooh and it's got me moving

172

Summer Romance

Just a few days and you'll be back in your school
I'll be sitting around by the swimming pool
You'll be studying history and you'll be down the
    gym
And I'll be down the pub, I'll be playing pool and
    drinking

It's over now, it's a summer romance and it's through
It's over now, it's a summer romance and it's through

Just a few days and you'll be back in your class
Sucking up the teacher and trying to get an "A" pass
You're trying to hide your make-up and you're trying
    to flash your legs
No sympathy from your spotty friends

It's over now

I need money so much, I need money so bad
And I can't be your mum, I don't wanna be your dad
I'm a serious man, I got serious lusts
Now I'll have to do away with the greasy kid stuff

It's over now

Ooh ooh, summer romance

173

Send It To Me

I think I've had enough
You know religion is tough
It's a state of mind I don't need
I'm sending a letter to my mother
I need some loving, send it to me
I lost my lover, unfaithful lover
I need some money, send it to me
I need consoling
Your boy's feeling lonely
Please try to phone me
Send it to me

Send it to me, send it to me, send it to me

If she can't travel, I can take a mule train
I can take the aeroplane, send it to me
I said I'm begging you, begging you, begging you
Down on my knees
Now please please please, you you
Got to send it, send it, send it
Send it to me, send it

Oh send it to me, send it to me, send it to me, send it
    to me

I'm sending a letter to my sister in Australia
Sister it reads, Ain't you got no daughter
No second cousin that needs my loving, send it to me

Send it to me, send it to me, send it to me, send it to
    me

She won't have to wash or scrape
She won't have to relocate
I guarantee her personal security
She don't have to be five foot ten
A blonde or a brunette
She don't have to be no social hostess
Send her

Send it to me, send it to me, send it to me, send it to
    me

She could be a Romanian
She could be a Bulgarian
She could be Albanian
She could be Hungarian
She might be Ukranian
She could be Australian
She could be the alien
Send it to me

Send it to me

174
Let Me Go

You're gonna get it straight from the shoulder
Can't you see the party's over
Let me go
Can't you get it through your thick head
Listen babe, we're finished, dead
Please let me go

I've tried giving you the velvet gloves
I've tried giving you the knockout punch
Let me go
Let me go
Let me go
Let me go
Let me go

I find it hard to be cruel
I find it hard to be cruel with a smile
Don't you know that you'll never find that perfect
Love that you read about
That you dream about

Maybe I'll become a play-boy
Hang around in gay bars
And move to the west side of town
You gonna get it straight from the shoulder
Can't you see the party's over
Let me go, let me go

So you think I'm giving you the brush-off
I'm just telling you to shove off
Hey! Please let me go
This ain't the time to waste my breath
We're going into sudden death
Hey, Let me go

Can't you get it through your thick head
This affair is dead as a do-do
The bell has rung and I've called time
The chair is on the table, (out the door baby)
Baby won't you let me go

Let me go
Baby won't you let me go
Let me go
Baby won't you let me go
Let me go

175
Indian Girl

Little Indian girl, where's your mama?
Little Indian girl, where is your papa?
He's fighting the war in the streets of Masaya
All the children were dead
'Cept the one girl who said
Please Mister Gringo
Please find my father
Lesson number one
Better learn while you're young

Life just goes on and on getting harder and harder
Little Indian girls from Nueva Granada

Ma says got no food
There's nothing left in the larder
Last piece of meat was eaten by the soldiers that
    raped her
Lesson number one
Better learn while you're young

Life just goes on and on getting harder and harder
Little Indian girls from Nueva Granada

If I saw them today
It's a sight I would say . . .

They're shooting down planes with their M16s and
    with laughter
Mister Gringo
My father, he ain't no Che Guevara

He's fighting the war in the streets of Masaya

Little Indian girl, where is your father?
Indian girl, where is your mama?
They're fighting for Mister Castro in the streets of
    Angola
La la la la

Where The Boys Go

Hey, girls you'd better listen to me
I'm getting starved of your company
All day Monday and all day Tuesday
I'm playing football, there's nothing on the tele

Ever since I was just thirteen years old
And I always felt shy but I acted so bold
Never had the money and never had the class
But I always seem to get myself a Saturday night
    piece of arse

Where the boys go on a Saturday night
Where the boys all go
Hold on tight, where the boys go
Saturday night where the boys all go

Saturday morning and you see me down the pub
And I piss away my money and I can't stand up
Three o'clock you'll see me in the road
Telling everybody where the boys all go

Hey, never keep a secret from me
Never keep a secret from you
Hey, never keep a secret from you

Where the boys go
Saturday night, where the boys all go
Hold on tight, where the boys go
Stand around and pose, where the boys all go
Showing off their clothes, where the boys go
Down the disco
Where the boys all go, where the boys all go

Hey you girls, what you doing tonight?
Do you want a dance or do you want a fight?
Listen here darling, I know the score
Paint your face, dye your hair, I'll see you round the
    back

Where the boys go
Saturday night, where the boys all go
Hold on tight, where the boys go
Saturday night, where the boys all go
There they go, there they go

Down In The Hole

Will all your money buy you forgiveness
Keep you from sickness or keep you from cold?
Will all your money keep you from madness
Keep you from sadness when you're down in the
    hole?

'Cause you'll be down in the gutter
You'll be begging for cigarettes,
Bumming for nylons in the American zone
You'll be down in the hole, down in the hole
No escape from trouble, nowhere to go

Down in the gutter
You'll be begging for cigarettes
Begging forgiveness, I'll let you know
You'll be down in the hole after digging the trenches
Looking for cover and finding that there is nowhere to
    go

None of your money will buy you forgiveness
None of your jewelry, none of your gold
Your black market cigarettes, your American
    nightclubs
They've got nowhere left

Something for nothing, oh all what your friends got
Something for nothing, yes that's all you know
There's something down in the hole, down in the
    hole
Something down in the hole

Emotional Rescue

Is there nothing I can say or nothing I can do
To change your mind, I'm so in love with you
You're deep in, you can't get out
You're just a poor girl in a rich man's world

Ooh, ooh
Baby I'm crying over you

Don't you know promises were never made to keep
Just like the night they dissolve in sleep
I'll be your saviour steadfast and true
I'll come to your emotional rescue
I'll come to your emotional rescue

Ooh

Yeah, here I am crying
Crying baby, yeah I'm crying
Yeah I'm crying babe
I'm like a child baby
Like a child
Yes I'm like a child, like a child, like a child like a
    child, ooh

You think you're one of a special breed,
You think that you're his pet Pekinese
I'll be your saviour steadfast and true
I'll come to your emotional rescue
I'll come to your emotional rescue

Ooh

I come to you so silent in the night
So stealthy, so animal quiet
I'll be your saviour steadfast and true
I'll come to your emotional rescue
I'll come to your emotional rescue

Ooh

Yeah, I was dreaming last night babe
Last night, I was dreaming you'd be mine
But I was crying like a child
Yeah I was crying
Crying like a child

You could be mine mine mine mine mine all mine
You could be mine
You could be mine
You could be mine all mine

Yes you could be mine, tonight and every night
I will be your knight in shining armour
Coming to your emotional rescue
You will be mine
I will be your knight in shining armour
Riding across the desert on a fine Arab charger

She's So Cold

I'm so hot for her
I'm so hot for her
I'm so hot for her and she's so cold
I'm so hot for her
I'm on fire for her
I'm so hot for her and she's so cold

I'm a burning bush
I'm a burning fire
I'm a bleeding volcano
But I'm so hot for her
I'm so hot for her
I'm so hot for her and she's so cold

Yes I've tried rewiring her
I've tried refiring her
I think her engine is permanently stalled
She's so cold, she's so cold
She's so cold, cold, cold like a tomb-stone
She's so cold, she's so cold
She's so cold, cold, cold like an ice-cream cone
She's so cold, she's so cold
When I touch her my hand just froze

I'm so hot for her, I'm so hot for her
I'm so hot for her
Put your hand on the heat, put your hand on the heat
And come on baby, let's go
She's so cold, she's so cold, cold
She's so c-c-c-c-c-cold but she's a beautiful girl

She's so cold, She's so cold
I think she was born in the Arctic Zone
She's so cold, she's so cold
When I touch her, my hand just froze
She's so cold, she's goddam cold
She's so cold, cold, cold she's so cold

Who would believe you were a beauty indeed
When the days get shorter and the nights get long
When the light fades and the rain comes
No-body will know
When you're old, when you're old
Nobody will know that
You were a beauty
A Sweet, sweet beauty
A Sweet, sweet beauty, but stone, stone cold
You're so cold, you're so cold, cold, cold,
You're so cold, you're so cold

All About You

Well if you call this a life
Why must I spend mine with you
If the show must go on
Let it go on without you
I'm so sick and tired hanging around with jerks like
   you

Who'll tell me those lies
And let me think they're true
What am I to do,
You want it
I got it too

The laughs may be cheap
That's just 'cause the joke's about you
I'm so sick and tired
Hanging around with dogs like you
You're the first to get laid
Always the last bitch to get paid

Who'll tell me no lies
And let me think they're true
I heard one or two
And they weren't about me
They weren't about her
They were all about you

I may miss you
But missing me just isn't you
I'm so sick and tired of hanging around dogs
Who'll tell me those lies
And let me think they're true
I heard one or two and they
Weren't about me
Weren't about you
They're all about you
All about you
So sick and tired
What should I do
You want
You get
So how come I'm still in love with you?

The Music

1

All Down The Line

Oh heard the wires a hummin'
All down the line.

Yeah heard the women sighin'
All down the line.

Oh hear the children cryin'
All down the line.

out and that's that! ———
Repeat and fade

Why put this sadness inside of me
Why be so matter of fact
Why put this one bit of hope in me?
You sold me out and that's that.

I hope that you're having fun with me
There's not much left to attack
I hope that you're nearly done with me
You sold me out and that's that.

3

Angie

CODA

An-gie — I still love you ba-by —

Ev-'rywhere I look — I see your eyes —

There ain't a wo-man that comes close to you

Come on ba-by dry your eyes — But

An-gie — An - gie

Ain't it good to be a-live —

Angie you're beautiful but ain't it time we said goodbye
Angie I still love you remember all those nights we cried
All the dreams we held so close seemed to all go up in smoke
Let me whisper in your ear Angie, Angie where will it lead us from here
Angie where will it lead us from here

Instrumental
Oh Angie don't you weep all your kisses still taste sweet
I hate that sadness in your eyes but
Angie, Angie ain't it time we said goodbye.

Instrumental
With no loving in our souls and no money in our coats
You can't say we're satisfied
But Angie Angie I still love you baby.

4

As Tears Go By

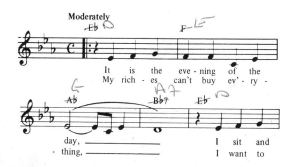

Moderately

It is the eve-ning of the
My rich - es can't buy ev'-ry-

day, _____ I sit and
- thing, _____ I want to

watch the chil-dren play. _____
hear the chil-dren sing _____

Smil-ing fac-es I can see — but not for
All I hear is the sound

me, — I sit and watch as tears go

by. _____ of rain-fall-ing

on the ground, I sit and watch as tears go

by. _____ It is the

eve-ning of the day, _____

I sit and watch the chil-dren play, _____

_____ Do-in' things I used to do _____

they think are new, _____ I sit and

watch as tears go by.

Mm

Mm

Mm _____

Back Street Girl

Don't want you part of my world _____ Just you be my Back Street Girl _____

6

Beast Of Burden

street, *Put me out*

A   E   B/D♯   C♯m

with no shoes on my feet, But put me out

A   E

B/D♯   C♯m   A   E

put me out   put me out of mis - e - ry, —

E   B/D♯   C♯m   A

Yeah

E   B/D♯   C♯   A

all your sick-ness I can   suck it up

E   E/D♯ C♯m   A

Throw it all at me, I can shrug it off,

E   B/D♯   C♯m

There's one thing that   I don't un - der -

A   E   E/G♯

stand,   You keep on   tell - ing me I

A   E   B/D♯ C♯m

ain't your kind of man, ain't I rough e - nough.

A   E   B/D♯ C♯m

Oh!   ain't I   tough e - nough,

A   E   B/D♯ C♯m

ain't I   rich e-nough, in love e - nough,

A   E   B/D♯ C♯m

Oooh ooh ___ please _____

A   E

— I'll nev - er be your Beast _

___ of Bur - den,   I'll nev - er

A

be your Beast ___ of Bur - den,

E   B/D♯   C♯m

nev-er, nev - er, nev-er, nev - er,   nev-er, nev - er,

A   E   B/D♯ C♯m   A   A/B

nev - er be _____

Before They Make Me Run

run.

Worked the bars and side-shows,
Along the Twilight Zone,
Only a crowd can make you feel so alone,
And it really hit home
Booze and pills and powders,
You have to choose your medicine,
Well, it's another good-bye,
To another good friend.

Watch my tail-lights fading,
There ain't a dry eye in the house,
They're laughin' and singin', well they're dancin'
and drinkin' as I left town.
I'm gonna find my way to Heaven,
'Cause I did my time in Hell
I wasn't looking too good, but I was feeling real well.

Bitch

Sometimes I'm sexy, more like a stud
Kicking the stall at night
Sometimes I'm so shy, got to be worked on
Don't have no bark or bite

9

Blue Turns To Grey

Moderately

So now that she is gone You
won't feel bad for long For may-be
just an ho-ur or just a mo-ment_
of the day - ay Then blue turns to
grey __ And try as you may __
You just don't feel_ good And you
don't feel all right __ And you know
that you must find her, find her, find her
find her Blue turns to
grey Blue turns to grey__ Blue turns to

Repeat and fade

You think you'll have a ball
And you won't hurt at all
You'll find another girl
Or maybe more to pass the time away
Then blue turns to grey
And try as you may
You just don't feel good
And you don't feel all right
And you know that you must
Find her find her find her

She's not home when you call
So then you go to all
All the places where she likes to be
But she has gone away
Then blue turns to grey
And try as you may
You just don't feel good
And you don't feel all right
And you know that you must
Find her find her find her

Brown Sugar

Moderate tempo

Gold___ Coast slave_ ship Bound for cot-ton fields,_ Sold___ in a mar-ket down in New Or-leans_ Scarred_ old slav-er know He's do-in' al-right__ Hear_____ _him whip the wom-en Just _ a-round mid-night Ah Brown Su-gar, how come you taste so good?___ (A-ha) Brown Su-gar, just like a young girl should __ A-huh.__

drums

I said yeah___ I said yeah_ I said yeah_ I said oh__ just like a just like a black girl should. I said yeah_

Repeat ad lib.

Drums beating
Cold English blood runs hot,
Lady of the house wondrin'
Where it's gonna stop
Houseboy knows
That he's doing alright
You should have heard him
Just around midnight

Brown sugar. . . . . . .

I bet your mama was
A tent show queen
And all her girl friends
Were sweet sixteen
I'm no schoolboy,
But I know what I like
You should have heard me
Just around midnight.

Brown sugar. . . . . . .

Can You Hear The Music

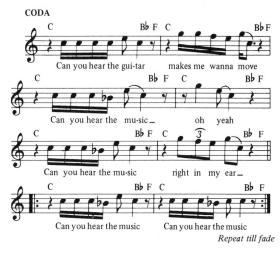

Sometimes you're feeling you've been pushed around
And your rainbow just ain't here
Don't you fear, don't you fear

When I hear the music, trouble disappears
When you hear the music ringing in your ears
Can you feel the magic floating in the air
Can you hear the magic, oh yeah

Can you hear the music
Can you hear the music
Can you feel the magic in the air
Can you feel the magic, oh yeah

Love is a mystery, I can't de-mystify, oh no
Sometimes I'm dancing on air
But I get scared, I get scared

When you hear the music, ringing in the air
Can you hear the music, oh yeah
Can you hear the drummer makes me gotta groove

Can you hear the guitar makes me wanna move
Can you hear the music, oh yeah
Can you hear the music, right in my ear
Can you hear the music (Fade)

12

Can't You Hear Me Knocking

Can't you hear me knocking when you're safe asleep
Can't you hear me knocking down the gas light street
Can't you hear me knocking throw me down the keys

Allright now

Hear me ringing big bells toll
Hear me singing soft and low

I've been begging on my knees

Casino Boogie

Moderate Blues

No good, — can't speak, wound up, — no sleep. Sky div - er in - side her, skip rope, — stunt fly - er. Wound - ed lov - er, got — no time on hand. — One last cy - cle, thrill freak Un - cle Sam. — Pause for bus - 'ness, hope you un - der - stand. — Judge and ju - ry walk out hand in hand. Die - trich mov - ies, close up boo - gies, kiss - ing cut in cans. Gro - tesque mu - sic, mil - li - on dol - lar sad. —

Got no tac - tics, got — no time on hand. — Left shoe shuf - fle, right shoe shuf - fle sink - ing in the sand. — Fade out free - dom, steam - ing heat on, Watch — that hat in black — Fin - ger twitch - ing, got — no time on hand.

Repeat and Fade

14

Child Of The Moon

The wind blows rain in-to my
face The sun glows at the end of the
high-way Child of the moon — rub your rain-y
eyes _____ Oh, child of the moon ___
_ Give me a wide-a-wake, cres-cent-shaped

1.
smile _____ She

2.
smile _____ The

3.
smile _____

She shivers, by the light she is hidden
She flickers, like a lamp lady vision
Child of the moon rub your rainy eyes
Child of the moon
Give me a wide-awake, crescent-shaped smile

The first car on the foggy road riding
The last star for my lady is pining
Child of the moon bid the sun arise
Child of the moon
Give me a misty day, pearly grey
Silver silky faced, wide-awake, crescent-
    shaped smile

15

Citadel

Moderate tempo

Men at arms shout, "Who goes there?"
We have jour-neyed far ___ from here _
Armed with bi-bles make ___ us swear _
Chorus:
Can-dy and Cath-y hope you both are
well Please come see me
in your cit-a-del _____

1. 2. 3.

4.

Flags are flying dollar bills
From the heights of concrete hills
You can't see the pinnacles

Chorus:

In the streets of many walls
Here the peasants come and crawl
You can hear their numbers called

Chorus:

Screaming people fly so fast
In their shiny metal cars
Through the woods of steel and glass

Chorus:

Coming Down Again

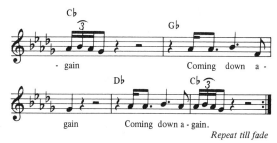

Coming down again, coming down again
On the ground again
Slipped my tongue in someone else's pie
Tasting better ev'ry time.
She turned green and tried to make me cry
Being hungry aint no crime

17

Complicated

Moderate Rock

Cm

She looks so sim-ple in her way — She

G7

does the same thing ev-'ry day — But she's

ded-i-cat - ed to hav-ing her own

Ab   Eb

way She's ver-y com-pli-cat - ed!

Bb Eb Bb7 Gm Bb7 │1. 2. 3. Bb Eb Bb7

Gm Bb7 │4. Bb Eb Bb7 Gm Bb7

Repeat and fade

Women seem to fill her mind
And many men in so short time
But she's underrated. She treats me oh so kind
She's very complicated

We talk together and discuss
What is really best for us
She's sophisticated. My head's fit to bust
'Cause she's so complicated

She knows just how to please her man
She's softer than a baby lamb
But she's very educated and doesn't give a damn
She's very complicated

18

Congratulations

Moderately slow

G   Em

Con-grat - u - la -tions

G   Em

con-grat - u - la - tions

G   Em

Well done — my friend

you've done it a - gain

C   D

You've gone and broke an - an-oth - er

G   D7

heart Yeah, you've tore it a-part

G   Em

you've done it be - fore

G   Em

hope you do it some more

C   D7

You've got it down — to a fine

G G7 C

art.   Re-mem-ber the

D7   G

first time— you tried to do it to

me   My girl won't fall ____

you wait and see you wait and see

Con-grat - u - la-tions ____

You've gone and broke an - an-oth - er

heart   Yeah, you   tore it a-part ____

Con - grat - u - la-tions ____

Repeat and fade

con-grat - u - la-tions ____

19

Connection

Repeat and fade

My bags they get a very close inspection
I wonder why it is that they suspect on
They're dying to add me to their collection
And I don't know if they'll let me go

Cool, Calm And Collected

Bright ragtime tempo

She's ver-y wealth-y it's true ___

___ So in that she is one up on you ___

___ She's dressed all in red, white and

blue ___ And she al-ways knows more

than you do ___ She's so af-

fect - ed, cool, calm, col - lect -

ed. 2) She ed. 3) She ed

She knows who to smile to today
She has just been brought up in that way
She knows all the right games to play
And she always just knows what to say
She's well respected
Cool, calm, collected

In public the strain's hard to bear
But she exudes such a confident air
But behind she is not without care
But she sweeps it right under her hair
She's well respected
Cool, calm, collected

She seems to glow brilliantly white
And her hair seems to shine in the night
With her feet unbelievably light
And her teeth ready sharpen to bite
She's so respected
Cool, calm, collected

Country Honk

Crazy Mama

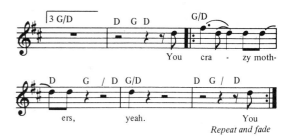

Well, your oldtime religion
Is just superstition.
You're gonna pay high prices
For your sacrifices, ah yeah.
All your blood and thunder
Sure can't faze me none.
If you gonna keep on coming
I'm gonna take it all head on.
And if you don't believe I'm gonna do it,
Just wait till you get hit by that bullet.
You're crazy, mother, ah yeah.

I'm coming down to get you now.
Don't think I ain't thought about it,
But it sure makes my shackles rise.
And coldblood murder,
It makes me want to draw the line.
Well, you're crazy, mother,
With your ball and chain.
You're plain psychotic, plain insane.
If you don't believe I'm gonna do it,
Just wait for the thud of the bullet.
You're crazy, mother, ah yeah.

23

Dance Little Sister

dance — lit - tle sis - ter dance —

dance — lit - tle sis - ter dance —

On Sat - ur - day night — we

don't go home we bacch - an - nal — there ain't —

— no dawn — Dance —

lit - tle sis - ter dance —

I said dance — Dance —

— lit - tle sis - ter dance — dance —

— lit - tle sis - ter dance — dance —

— lit - tle sis - ter dance —

1. 2. *D.S. (Instrumental and Fade)*

I said dance —

It make me hot I'm wet with sweat,
It burns like hell, I've four hours left,
Dance dance little sister dance
Get next to me drive me close,
Don't mamaguay me I lose control,

Chorus

Dancing With Mr. D

Will it be poison in my glass
Will it be slow or will it be fast
The bite of a snake, the sting of a spider
A drink of belladonna of a Toussaint night.
Hiding round a corner in New York city
Looking down a 44 in West Virginia
I was dancing, dancing, dancing so free
I was dancing, dancing, dancing so free
Dancing with Mister D.

Mister D. Mister D. Mister D. Mister D.
Dancing, dancing, dancing, dancing,
Dancing, dancing, dancing, dancing,

Dancing, dancing dancing so free
I was dancing, dancing, dancing, so free
Dancing Lord take your hands off me
Dancing with Mister D. Mister D. Mister D.

One night I was dancing with a lady in black
Wearing black silk gloves and a black silk hat
She looked at me longing with black velvet eyes
She gazed at me strange all cunning and wise
Then I saw the flesh just fall off her bones
The eyes in her skull were just burning like coals
Lord have mercy fire and brimstone
I was dancing with Mister D.
Dancing, dancing, dancing so free
I was dancing, dancing, dancing so free
Dancing Lord take your hands off me
Dancing with Mister D.

Dandelion

One o'clock, two o'clock, three o'clock, four
    o'clock, five
Dandelions don't care about the time
Dandelions don't tell no lies
Dandelions will make you wise
Tell me if she laughs or cries
Blow away dandelion...

So you're older now. Just the same
You can play the dandelion game
When you've finished with your childlike prayers
Well, you know you should wear it

Tinker, tailor, soldier, sailor's life
Rich man, poor man, beautiful doctor's wife
Dandelions don't tell no lies
Dandelions will make you wise
Tell me if she laughs or cries
Blow away dandelion...

Little girls and boys come out to play
Bring your dandelions to blow away
Dandelions don't tell no lies
Dandelions will make you wise
Tell me if she laughs or cries
Blow away dandelion...

Dead Flowers

Well, when you're sitting back
In your rose pink cadillac
Making bets on Kentucky Derby Day
I'll be in my basement room
With a needle and a spoon
And another girl can take my pain away

Chorus:

Dear Doctor

Moderate Waltz

Oh help me, dear doc-tor, I'm dam-aged _____ There's a pain _____ where there once ____ was a heart _____ It's sleep-ing_ it's beat-ing_ Can't you please take it out and pre-serve it right there in that jar _____ Oh, help me please ma-ma I'm sick-'ning_____ it's to-day____ that's the day of the plunge_____ Oh the gal _____ I'm to mar-ry is a bow-leg-ged sow I've been soak-ing up drink like a

sponge_____ "Don't you wor-ry, get dressed" cried my moth-er_____ As she plied me with Bour-bon so so-ur____ ____ "Pull your socks up, Put your suit on, Comb your long hair down For you will be wed in the ho-ur"____ Oh, help me, dear doc-tor, I'm dam-aged_____ There's a pain ____ where there once____ was a heart _____ It's sleep-ing _ It's beat-ing_ Can't you please take it out and pre-serve it right there in the

jar_____ I was trem-bling as I

put on my jack-et _____ It had

creas-es as sharp as a knife_____

_____ I put the ring in my pock-et

but there was a note And my heart

it jumped in-to my mouth _____

It read, "Dar-ling I'm sor-ry to

hurt you_____ but I've no cour-age

to speak to your face_____ but I'm

down in Vir-gin-ia with your cous-in

Lou and there'll be no wed-ding to-

day"_____ So help me, dear

doc-tor, I'm dam-aged_____ You can

put back my heart ___ in its hole_____

_____ Oh ma-ma, I'm cry-ing

tears of re-lief and my pulse is now

un-der con-trol_____

28

Don'cha Bother Me

Don't Lie To Me

Verse 1&4,5 A

Well let's talk it ov-er babe, be-fore we start _ I heard a-bout the way you used to do your part _ Don't lie to me _ Don't you lie _ to me. Don't you make _ me mad _ I'll get ev-il as a / I'm as shook-up man can be _ well

Well all the kinds of people that I just can't stand
That's a lyin' woman and a cheatin' man
Don't lie to me, don't you lie to me.
Don't you make me mad.
I'll get evil as a man can be.

Well I could love you baby and it ain't no lie
For every winter till the well runs dry
Don't lie to me, don't you lie to me
Don't you make me mad
I'm as shook up as a man can be.

Well let's talk it over babe before we start
I heard about the way you do your part
Don't lie to me, don't you lie to me.
Don't you make me mad.
I'll get evil as a man can be.

Doo Doo Doo Doo Doo
(Heartbreaker)

Downtown Suzie

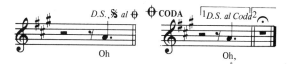

(repeat of letter A)

    Lying on a naked bed.
        yeah, yeah, yeah
    With an Alka Seltzer head.
        yeah, yeah.

(repeats at letter B)

1. I heard the ringing of the bell.
        yeah, yeah, yeah
    It's Lucy with the cleaning towel.
        yeah, yeah.

2. Oh, I'm feelin' like the Sunday Times,
        yeah, yeah, yeah.
    A Southern California wine.
        yeah, yeah.

3. Lucy kicked me in the hole.
        yeah, yeah, yeah.
    Tennis worth of achin' bones
        Ooh - ooh.

32

Each And Every Day Of The Year

what my life's for,   Yes,   I   do,

yes I do, yes I do, yes I do

Each ____ and ev-'ry day ____

____ of the year ____

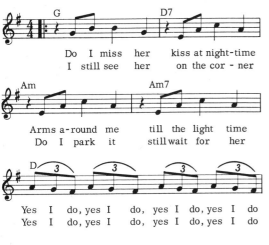

Do I miss her   kiss at night-time
I still see her   on the cor-ner

Arms a-round me   till the light   time
Do I park it   still wait for   her

Yes I do, yes I   do, yes I do, yes I do
Yes I do, yes I   do, yes I do, yes I do

Each ____ and ev-'ry day ____
Each ____ and ev-'ry day ____

1.
____ of the year ____
of the year ____

2.
year ____

Nev-er get a - round an - y - more

Don't know what my friends are for

No fun sit-tin' ____ all a - lone but I'll

cry, cry, cry on my own   Now that she has

gone for ev - er   Do I won - der

Empty Heart

Well you've been my lover for a long long time
Well you've been my lover for a long long time
'Cos you lived all alone in my town
I want my love again (repeat)

An empty heart is like an empty life
I said an empty heart is like an empty life
It makes you feel
Like you wanna cry (repeat)

34

Factory Girl

Waiting for a girl and she's got stains all down her dress,
Waiting for a girl and my feet are getting wet,
She ain't come out yet,
Waiting for a factory girl.

Waiting for a girl and her knees are much too fat,
Waiting for a girl who wears scarves instead of hats,
Her zipper's broken down the back,
Waiting for a factory girl.

35

Family

Here comes the girl, she's got her head screwed on
But it ain't screwed on right
Her ambition is to be a prostitute
But the breaks just weren't right.

What exactly's gonna happen
When her father finds out
That his virgin daughter has bordello dreams
And that he's the one she wants to try out.

Here's ma, she's living dangerously
As I said she'll try anything twice
She thinks she can run right to the whirlpool's edge
And stop herself just in time

What exactly's gonna happen
When she finally fizzles out
And her lovers will just be sucked into
To see what the colours of death are all about.

Here's the son, guess his legs are screwed on
Yeh, they're screwed on pretty tight
But his brain, loose and it ain't no use
He's already lost the fight.

What exactly's gonna happen
When he's finally realised
That he can't play his guitar like E.G. Jim
Or write St. Augustine if he tried.

LAST CHORUS
That there's gonna happen
When the family finds out
And they've been in the middle of it now for a thousand years
And need a thousand more to climb out.

Faraway Eyes

I had an arrangement to meet a girl but I was kind of late and
I thought by the time I got there she'd be off – she'd be off with
the nearest truck driver she could find:
Much to my surprise, there she was sitting in the corner (a little
bleary eyed – worse for wear and tear) was the girl with
faraway eyes.

Chorus
So if you're down on your luck and you can't harmonize
Find a girl with faraway eyes
And if you're downright disgusted and life ain't worth a dime,
Get a girl with faraway eyes.

Well the preacher kept right on saying that all I had to do was send
Ten dollars to the Church of the Sacred Bleeding Heart of Jesus
Located somewhere in Los Angeles, California, and next week they'd
Say my prayer on the radio and all my dreams would come true.
So I did and next week I got a prayer for the girl, well you
know what kind of eyes she's got . . .

Chorus
So if you're down on your luck I know y'all sympathize,
Find a girl with faraway eyes.
And if you're downright disgusted and life ain't worth a dime
Get a girl with faraway eyes.
So if you're down on your luck I know y'all sympathize,
Get a girl with faraway eyes.

Fingerprint File

Fingerprint file you get me down,
You get me running keep me on the ground
Know my moves,
Way ahead of time,
List'ning to me on your satellite.

Feeling followed feeling tagged,
Crossing water trying to wipe my tracks
And there's some little jerk in the F.B.I.
A-keeping papers on me six feet high,
It gets me down, it gets me down.

Better watch out on your telephone
Wrong number they know you ain't home
You know my habits,
Way ahead of time,
List'ning to me on your satellite.

Keep a look-out - electric eyes,
Rats on the sell-out who gonna testify.
You know my habits,
Way ahead of time,
List'ning to me on your satellite.

Flight 505

Well, I confirmed my reservation then I hopped a cab
No idea of my destination and feeling pretty bad
With my suitcase in my hand, in my head my new life
And then I told the airline girl
Well get me on flight number 505
Get me on flight number 505

Well, I sat right there in my seat well feeling like a
    king
With the whole world right at my feet of course I'll
    have a drink
But suddenly I saw that we never ever would arrive
He put the plane down in the sea
The end of flight number 505
The end of flight number 505

Fool To Cry

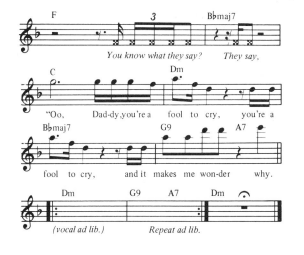

You know I got a woman,
And she live in a poor part of town,
And I go see her sometimes
And we make love so fine.
I put my head on her shoulder.
She says, "Tell me all your troubles."
You know what she says? She say,

Chorus

(Vocal ad lib.)
I'm a fool, baby,
I'm a fool, baby,
I'm a certified fool, now
I want to tell ya,
Gotta tell ya, baby.
I'm a fool, baby,
Certified fool for ya, mama, come on,
I'm a fool, I'm a fool,
I'm a fool.

Get Off Of My Cloud

Repeat and fade

The telephone is ringin'. I say "Hi it's me, who's
    there on the line?"
A voice says "hi hullo. How are you?" Well I
    guess I'm doing fine
He says "It's three a.m. and there's too much noise,
    don't you people ever want to go to bed?
Just 'cause you feel so good, do you have to drive me
    out of my head?"
I said,"hey you get off of my cloud, hey you get off
    of my cloud
Hey you get off of my cloud, don't hang around
'Cause two's a crowd on my cloud baby"

I was sick and tired, fed up with this and decided to
    take a drive down town
It was so very quiet and peaceful. There was nobody,
    not a soul around
I laid myself out I was so tired and I started to dream
In the mornin' the parkin' tickets were just like flags
    stuck on my wind screen
I said,"hey you get off of my cloud, hey you get off of
    my cloud
Hey, you get off of my cloud, don't hang around
'Cause two's a crowd on my cloud baby"

Gimmie Shelter

it's just a shot a-way   it's just a

shot a-way   It's just a   shot a-way

it's just a shot a-way

Love, ___ sis - ter, ___

it's just a kiss a-way   it's just a

kiss a-way   it's just a kiss a-way

It's just a kiss a-way   it's just a

kiss a-way   It's just a   kiss a-way

Repeat and fade

Goin' Home

All those letters ev'ry day
Maybe allright in their way
But I'd love to see your face
When I get home in their place

Chorus:

I'm going home, I'm going home
I'm going home, I'm going home
I'm going home, I'm going home
Home bam bam bam ba back home
Yeah back home

When you're three thousand miles away
I can never sleep the same
If I packed my things right now
I could be home in seven hours

Chorus:

I'm going home, I'm going home
I'm going home, I'm going home
I'm going home bam bam bam ba bam
Home bam bam bam ba back home
Yeah back home

Gomper

Good Times, Bad Times

Very slow

There-'ve been good times There-'ve been bad times I've had my share of hard times, too — But I lost my faith in the world — hon-ey — when I lost you — Re-mem-ber the good times — we had to-geth-er — Don't you want them — back a-gain — Tho' these hard times are bug-ging me now I know now it's — the same — There's got-ta be

There's gotta be trust in this world
Or it won't get very far
Well trust in someone
Or just gonna be war

Gotta Get Away

Moderately

Ba-by, the truth is out — so don't de-ny — Ba-by, To think I be-lieved — all your lies — Dar-lin', I can't stand to see your face — It's the truth ya un-der-stand — I got to get a-way Got to get a-way — Got-ta, got-ta, got-ta get a-way — Got-ta get a-way —

Grown Up Wrong

Baby, I don't want to live here no more
Baby, so I've torn your pictures off my wall
Darlin' this old room is fallin' in on me
You understand the truth then
I got to get away, got to get away
Gotta, gotta, gotta get away
Got to get away

Baby, oh how could you take away your clothes
Baby, don't screw up this old pot of gold
Darlin' this old room of mine is all so fair
You understand me dear
I got to get away, got to get away
Gotta, gotta, gotta get away
Got to get away

Really grown up on me	Well, you grown up too fast
Well, you grown up on me	Well, you grown up too fast
Don't believe what I see	Don't forget about the past
Well, you grown up on me	Well, you grown up too fast
Well, you look so sweet	Well, you won't feel blue
When you're in your seat	When I'm through with you
But you grown up on me	But you grown up too fast

Hand Of Fate

'Cos my sweet girl was once his wife,
And he had papers that the judge had signed.
The wind blew hard, it was a stormy night;
He shot me once but I shot him twice.
The hand of fate is on me now;
It picked me up and it kicked me right down.
Kicked me right down, kicked me right down.

He was a bar-room man the violent kind;
He had no love for that gal of mine.
And then one day in a drinking bout,
He swore he'd throw me right out of town.
The hand of fate is on me now;
I shot that man , I put him underground.
I put him underground, underground, yes I did.

I'm on the run, I hear the hounds;
My luck is up, my chips are down.
So goodbye, baby, so long now;
Wish me luck I'm gonna need it child.
The hand of fate is on me now;
Yeah, it's too late, baby.
Too late, baby, too late now,

Vocal ad lib
Oh, yeah, man, yeah, yes, it is.
It's heavy now, heavy now.
The hand of fate is heavy now.
It picked me up and knocked me down.

48

Happy

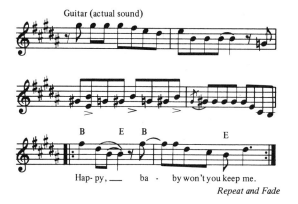

Guitar (actual sound)

Hap- py, ___ ba - by won't you keep me.

Repeat and Fade

49

Have You Seen Your Mother, Baby

shad-ow?___ Where have you been all your

life?_____ Talk - ing a -

bout all the peo - ple_____ who would

try _____ an - y - thing twice _____

1. 2

2. 4

Have you seen your mother, baby, standing in the
     shadow?
Have you had another baby standing in the shadow
You take your choice at this time
The brave old world or the slide to the depths of
     decline

50

Heart Of Stone

Slowly

There've been so man-y girls that I've known I've made so man-y cry And still I won-der why Here comes the lit-tle girl I see her walk-ing down the street She's all by her-self Try-ing so hard to please But__ she'll nev-er break nev-er break, nev-er break, Nev-er break This heart of stone Oh, no, no, this heart of stone__ What's diff-'rent a-bout__ her? I

don't real-ly know No mat-ter how I try I just can't make her cry But__ she'll nev-er break, Nev-er break, nev-er break, Nev-er break this heart of stone Oh, no, no, no,__ this heart of stone __ __ Don't keep on stone _ You'll nev-er break this heart of stone __

Don't keep on looking that same old way
If you try acting sad
You'll only make me glad
Better listen little girl
You go walking down the street
I ain't got no love
I ain't the kind to meet
But you'll never break
Never break, never break,
Never break this heart of stone
Oh, no, no
You'll never break this heart of stone

Hey Negrita

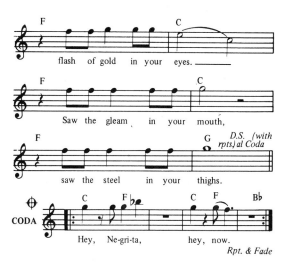

Come si chiama, what's your game?
I'm just a poor man; what's your name?
Shake your body, do it up now.
Shake your body, move it up now.

(Chorus)
(Bridge)

Baté las caderas, do it up now.
Just a momentita, not so fast.
I need money for my need is fast.

Listen, I'm a poor man, my pay is low.
Here's one last dollar and then we go.
One last dollar, I've got my pride.
I'm gonna call ya boss, boy, gonna tan your hide.

(Chorus)

Hide Your Love

Oh babe I'm sinking I wanna cry
Well I been drinking but now I'm dry
Why do ya hide, why do ya hide yer love
Now look here baby you sure look cheap
I make it mama seven days a week
Why do ya hide where do ya hide ya love,
Why do you hide it baby
Hide from the man that you love.

Oh yeah, Oh yeah,
Oh yeah, Oh yeah,
Why do you hide, why do you hide ya love
C'mom, c'mon, c'mon,
C'mon, c'mon, c'mon.

53

Oh Lord I'm reaching, reaching high
Oh babe I'm falling right out the sky
Why do ya hide, where do ya hide ya love
Why do ya hide it baby
Hide from the man you love
Oh yeah, Oh yeah,
Oh yeah, Oh yeah,
Why do ya hide why do ya hide your love
Why do ya hide it baby
Hide from the man that you love.

High And Dry

One minute I was up there standing by her side
The next I was down here well left out of the ride
High and dry oh what a way to go
She left me standing here just high and dry

Anything I wish for I only had to ask her
I think she found out it was money I was after
High and dry oh what a weird let-down
She left me standing here just high and dry

Lucky that I didn't have any love towards her
Next time I'll make sure that the girl will be
          much poorer
High and dry oh what a way to go
She left me standing here just high and dry

Honky Tonk Women

Repeat and fade

Hot Stuff

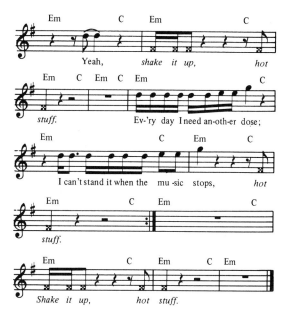

Everybody on the dance floor,
You know what I'm talking about.
Music make you forget all your troubles,
Make you sing and make it tell the whole wide world.
So what, hot stuff, shake it up.

I want to tell all my friends in London
There ain't nothing wrong with you,
But you'd better shape up.
Shake it up, you're hot stuff.

All the people in New York City
I know you're going broke,
But I know you're tough.
Yeah, you're hot stuff.

To everybody in Jamaica that's working in the sun,
You're hot, you're hot, you're hot stuff.
Shake it up, shake it up,
Hot stuff, hot stuff.

56

I Am Waiting

where   Oh we're   wait - ing   Oh we're...

Repeat and fade

You can't hold out, you can't hold out, oh yeah, oh
     yeah
Waiting for someone to come out of somewhere

See it come along and don't know where it's from
Oh, yes, we will find out
Well it happens all the time
It's censored from our mind, we'll find out

Slow or fast, slow or fast, oh yeah, oh yeah
End at last, end at last, oh yeah, oh yeah
Waiting for someone to come out of somewhere
Stand up coming hears and destilation fears
Oh, yes, we will find out
Well like a withered stone
Fears will piece your bones, you'll find out

Oh we're waiting, oh we're waiting, oh yeah, oh
     yeah
Waiting for someone to come out of somewhere

I Got The Blues

Chorus:

In the arms of a guy
Who will bring you alive
Won't drag you down with abuse

Chorus:

In the silk sheet of time
I will find peace of mind
Love is a bed full of blues   (to Coda)

If You Can't Rock Me

Now who's that black girl in the bright blue hair
Oh yeah
Now don't you know that it's rude to stare
Oh yeah
I'm not so green but I'm feelin' so fresh
I simply love to put her to the test
She's so alive and she's dressed to kill.
If you can't rock me, etc.

(8 bars Instrumental)
And there ain't nothing like a perfect mate
And I ain't lookin' for no wedding cake
But I been talking 'bout it much too long *(to coda)*

If You Let Me

Yes you're younger than I thought
You're so tall and I'm so short
It doesn't matter anyhow
But I'll let you guess .... (etc.)

It's a brand new thing for me
Loving you so physically
The time has come to say goodnight
But I'll let you guess .... (etc.)

Verse

You don't real-ly un-der-stand,

How it feels to be your

man, You're just nice to have a-

round But I'll let you guess

you can — get me if you

let me oh

yes. (Gtr.

)

Do Do— Do Do Do Do — Do Do

1,2,3,4   5

Do (Bass ———)

It's nice to talk to you today
It's very pleasant anyway
Is this as far as you will go?
But I'll let you guess .... (etc.)

instrumental until ....
You can get me if you let me, oh .... Yes ....

If You Really Want To Be My Friend

I know that ev'rybody wants to be your man
I don't want to tie you up,
Go ahead you're free,
And I never want to scar you with my brand,
We could live it up just you and me.

If you really want to understand a man,
Let him off the lead,
Sometimes set him free.
If you really, really want to be my friend
Give me the look of love not jealousy.

I really want to be your friend
Just a little faith is all we need
I don't want no dog eat dog world
For you and me get your nails out stop bleedin' me,
I know you think that life is a thriller (a thriller)   etc.

61

I'm All Right

I'm Free

I'm free to choose who I see any old time
I'm free to bring who I choose any old time
Love me, hold me, love me, hold me,
I'm free any old time to get what I want

I'm Going Down

Hey babe, what's your story? Tell
The good Lord gonna ring your front door bell.
I said shoot, babe, shoot your mother-in-law, yeah.
Alright, shoot her, yeah, right down girl.

In Another Land

We walked across the sand and the sea and the sky
And the castles were blue
I stop and hold your hand and the spray through the
         pine
And the feathers floated by
I stood and held your hand
And nobody else's hand will ever do
Nobody else will do

And I awoke was this some kind of joke
Much to my surprise I opened my eyes

We heard the trumpets blow and the sky turned grey
And I had to take this day
But I didn't know how I came to be there
When I'm fast asleep in bed
I stood and held your hand
And nobody else's hand will ever do
Nobody else will do

And I awoke was this some kind of joke
Much to my surprise I opened my eyes

It's Not Easy

It's a hard (it's not easy)
Yes it's hard (it's not easy)
It's a very hard thing
It's not easy
It's not easy living on your own

There's no place where you can call home
You've got me running like a cat in a thunderstorm
Just a big bed and a telephone
Like the last remnants of a stately home

It's a hard (it's not easy)
Yes it's hard (it's not easy)
It's a very hard thing
It's not easy
It's not easy living on your own

Sit here thinking with your head on fire
Go think the same thing you never tire
Imagining the glow of her long clean hair
As she goes to sit on her own high chair

It's a hard (it's not easy)
Yes it's hard (it's not easy)
It's a very hard thing
It's not easy
It's not easy living on your own

It's Only Rock 'N' Roll

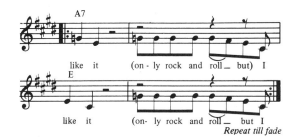

like it (on‑ly rock and roll _ but) I

like it (on‑ly rock and roll _ but I

Repeat till fade

If I could stick a knife in my heart
Suicide right on the stage
Would it be enough for your teenage lust
Would it help ease the pain, ease your brain
If I could dig down deep in my heart
Feelings would flood on the page
Would it satisfy ya, would it slide on by ya,
Would you think the boy's insane
He's insayayane.

67

Jigsaw Puzzle

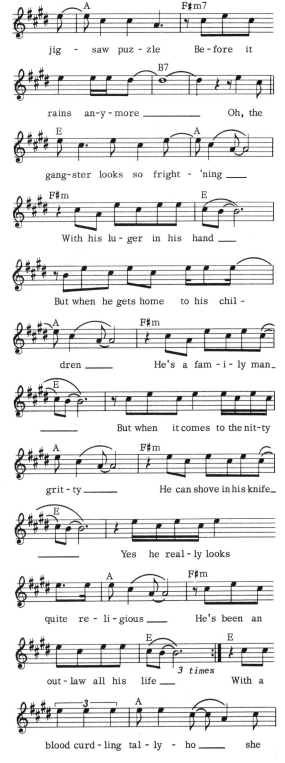

68

Jivin' Sister Fanny

F#m E
charged in-to the ranks — And blessed all —
— those grand - mas — who, with their
F#m
dy - ing breath_screamed "thanks!" —

Chorus:
E F#m
I'm — wait-ing so pa-tient-
A B7
ly I'm a-ly-ing on — the floor
E A
I'm just try'n' to do my jig - saw
F#m
puz - zle Be - fore it rains
B7
an-y more _____

Repeat and fade

Me I'm waiting so patiently lying on the floor
I'm just tryin' to do my jigsaw puzzle
Before it rains any more

Oh, the singer looks so angry
At being thrown to the lions
And the bass player looks so nervous
About the girls outside
And the drummer he was shattered
Trying to keep on time
And the guitar player looks damaged
They've been outcasts all their lives

Me I'm waiting so patiently lying on the floor
I'm just tryin' to do my jigsaw puzzle
Before it rains any more

And as twenty thousand grandmas
Wave their hankies in the air
All burning up their pensions
And shouting, 'It's not fair'
There's a regiment of soldiers
Standing, looking on
And the Queen is bravely shouting
'What the hell is going on?'

Verse 1 & 3
D
Jiv-ing sis-ter Fan-ny that's the
C D
name of the girl I love, —
uh uh uh uh. She
D
e-ven got me goin' out-a town down the
D
wrong high-way, — uh uh
D
uh. She got me walk-in' round
D
she's got me go-in' down "Hey". said the
C
po-lice-man,— get your sis-ter out of town.
D C
ooh child — you got me walking down the wrong highway,
D
— uh uh — uh Now

Repeat to Fade

Now jiving sister Fanny's got the brain of a dinosaur, uh uh uh uh
Yes, she's my fancy mother, and she hocked my electric guitar uh uh uh uh
She got the wrong way around, she's got me out of town.
She got me walkin' round (etc.)

69

Jumpin' Jack Flash

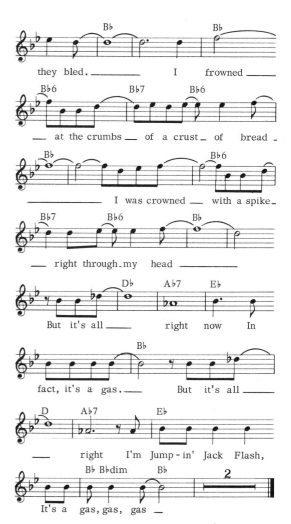

I was raised by a toothless bearded hag
I was schooled with a strap across my back
But it's all right now
In fact, it's a gas
But it's all right
I'm Jumpin' Jack Flash
It's a gas, gas, gas

Just Want To See His Face

Lady Jane

My sweet La - dy Jane

When I see you a - gain

Your ser-vant am I

And will hum-bly re- main

Just heed this plea my love On bend-ed

knees my love I pledge my - self to

La - dy Jane.

My dear La - dy Jane

My dear Lady Anne
I've done what I can
I must take my leave
For promised I am
This play is run my love
Your time has come my love
I've pledged my troth to Lady Jane

Oh my sweet Marie
I wait at your ease
The sands have run out
For your lady and me
Wedlock is nigh my love
Her station's right my love
Life is secure with Lady Jane

Let It Bleed

dream on me _____ I was

dream-ing of a steel__ gui-tar__ en-gage-

ment _____ When you drunk my health__

__ in scent-ed jas-mine tea _____

Yeah, you knifed__ me in my filth -

y dirt-y base - ment_

With that jad-ed, fad-ed junk-y nurse

Oh__ what pleas-ant com-pa-ny

We all need____ some-one

we can feed__ on _____ And if you

want to _ Well, you can feed on me__

_____ Take my arm__

take my leg_ Oh, ba-by don't you

take my head_

Well, we all__

_____ Get it on rid-er

get it on rid-er

get it on rid-er You can

bleed all o - ver me _____

Let It Loose

Let it all come down to- night.

Keep those tears hid out of sight,

let it loose, let it all come down.

Let it loose, let it all come down,

let it loose, let it all come down,

let it loose, let it all come down.

(repeat and fade)

Let's Spend The Night Together

now   Let's

spend the night ___ to - geth - er

I feel so strong that I can't disguise
(Oh my, let's spend the night together)
But I just can't apologise
(Oh no, let's spend the night together)
Don't hang me up and don't let me down
We could have fun just grooving around
(Around and around oh my, my)
Let's spend the night together
Now I need you more than ever
Let's spend the night together
Let's spend the night together
Now I need you more than ever

You know I'm smiling, baby
You need some guiding, baby
I'm just deciding, baby
Now I need you more than ever
Let's spend the night together
Let's spend the night together now

This doesn't happen to me ev'ry day
(Oh my, let's spend the night together)
No excuses offered anyway
(Oh my, let's spend the night together)
I'll satisfy your ev'ry need
And now I know you will satisfy me
(Oh my, my, my, oh my)
Let's spend the night together
Now I need you more than ever
Let's spend the night together now

Lies

Medium Rock

1. Lies,— drip - ing off your mouth like dirt.—

Lies, —— lies —

— in ev - 'ry step you got - ta walk

Lies, — whis - pered sweet - ly in my ear.—

Lies —— how

do do I get out of here. ——

Why, —— why— you have to be so cru -

- el. —— Lies, lies,— lies —

— I ain't such a fool. ————

To Coda

Lies, —— lies — you dir - ty Jez - e - bel. —

—— Why, why,— why,—

D. % al Coda

— why don't you go to Hell. —
6 times 3,4,5,6,ad lib.

CODA

Li, li, li, li,— li, li, li,— li, li, lies..

— li, li, lies. —— Lies, lies,— lies,—

— lies, lies, lies,

Lies — lies in my Poppa's looks
Lies — lies in my History books
Lies — lies like they teach in class
Lies, lies, lies I catch on way too fast
Fire, fire upon your wicked tongue
Lies, lies, lies you're trying to spoil my fun.

Little By Little

Live With Me

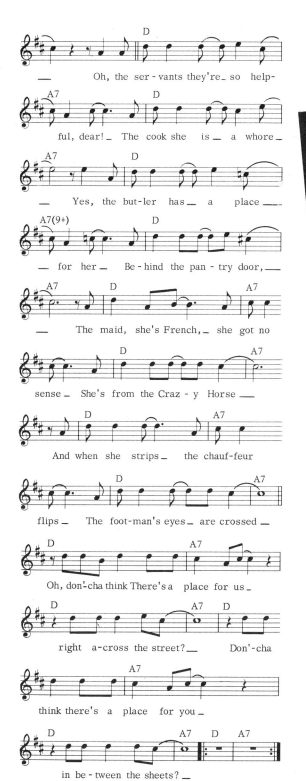

Oh, the ser-vants they're_ so help-ful, dear! The cook she is_ a whore_ Yes, the but-ler has_ a place _ for her _ Be-hind the pan-try door, _ The maid, she's French, _ she got no sense _ She's from the Craz - y Horse _ And when she strips _ the chauf-feur flips _ The foot-man's eyes _ are crossed _ Oh, don'-cha think There's a place for us _ right a-cross the street? _ Don'-cha think there's a place for you _ in be - tween the sheets? _

Repeat and fade

78

Long, Long While

change _ your mind _ Won't you change _

your mind _ I was wrong -er _____

_ you were right oh!

Love In Vain

80

Loving Cup

I'm the man who walks the hillside in the sweet summer sun.
I'm the man that brings you roses when you ain't got none.
Well, I can run and jump and fish but I won't fight
You, if you want to push and pull with me all night.
Give me a little drink from your loving cup.
Just one drink and I'll fall down drunk.

81

Luxury

I think it's such a strange thing, giving me concern
Half the world it got a nothing,
The other half got money to burn.
My woman need a new dress,
My daughter got to go to school,
I'm working so hard, I'm working for the company
I'm working so hard
I'm working so hard oh yeah oh yeah (8 bars Instrumental)
Now listen I'm a proud man, not a beggar walking on the street
I'm working so hard to keep you from the poverty
I'm working so hard to keep you in the luxury

Working on a Sunday in refinery
Make a million for the Texans Twenty dollar me
All the rum I want to drink it, I got responsibility
I'm working so hard to keep you from the poverty
I'm working so hard I'm working for the company
Working so hard I'm working so hard harder harder working working

Harder harder working working working harder harder Working
(4 times)

82

Melody

I took her out dancing,
But she drank away my cash;
She said "I'm gonna fix my face,
Don't you worry ,I'll be back."
I'm looking for her high and low
Like a mustard for a ham;
She was crashed out in the bathroom
In the arms of my best friend.

Then one day she left me,
She took ev'rything that moved;
My car, she took my trailer home
She took my Sunday boots.
My nose is on her trail,
I'm gonna catch her by surprise;
And then I'm gonna have the pleasure
To roast that child alive.

Memo From Turner

When the old men do all the fighting and the young men all look on
And the young girls eat their mother's meat from tubes of plasticon
Be wary of these my gentle friends of all the skin you breed
To have that tasty habit, it's not the hands that bleed.

Memory Motel

She drove a pick-up truck painted green and blue;
The tyres were wearing thin, she done a mile or two.
And when I asked her where she headed for,
"Back up to Boston, I'm singing in a bar."
I got to fly today on down to Baton Rouge;
My nerves are shot already, the road ain't all that smooth.
Across in Texas is the rose of San Antone;
I keep on a-feeling that gnawing in my bones.

Chorus

On the seventh day my eyes were all aglaze;
We been ten thousand miles and been in fifteen states.
Every woman seemed to fade out of my mind;
I hit the bottle and I hit the sack and cried.
What's all this laughter on the twenty-second floor?
It's just some friends of mine and they're busting down the doors.
It's been a lonely night at the Memory Motel.

Chorus

85

Midnight Rambler

Oh, don't do   that   Oh, don't do

that   Oh, don't do   that

Did you

(spoken:)

throat,   ba - by, And it   hurts!

Did you hear about the midnight rambler?
He'll leave his footprints up and down your hall
A-did you hear about the midnight gambler?
A-did you see me make my midnight call?

And if you ever catch the midnight rambler
I'll steal your mistress from under your nose
Well, go easy with your cold fandango
I'll stick my knife right down your throat, baby
And it hurts!

Miss Amanda Jones

With a rock beat

Down and down she goes —

Lit-tle Miss A-man-da Jones.— I said,

Down and down— and down— and down —

— She'd look real-ly love-ly at home

— Till some-bod-y gon-na come up and ask.

— her To live hap-pi-ly ev-er af-

ter, Miss A-man-da Jones —

Hey, girl, don't you re-al-ize—

— The mon-ey in-vest-ed in you —

Hey, girl, you've just got to find— some-

one who'll real-ly pull your fam-i-ly

through — Up and up she goes,—

— The Hon. A-man-da Jones —

Up and up— and up— and up— She

looks de-light-ful-ly stoned — She's the

dar-ling of the dis-co-theque crowd —

But of her line-age she's right-ful-ly proud.

— Miss A-man-da Jones —

'Round and 'round and 'round

Repeat and fade

On and on she goes
Little Miss Amanda Jones
I said on and on and on and on
Just watch her as she grows
Don't want to say it very obviously
But she's losing her nobility
Miss Amanda Jones

Hey girl, don't you realize
The money invested in you
Hey girl, you've just got to find someone
Who'll really pull your family through

Up and up she goes
The Hon. Amanda Jones
I said up and up and up and up
She looks quite delightfully stoned
She's the darling of the discotheque crowd
Of her lineage she's rightfully proud
Miss Amanda Jones

Hey girl, with your nonsense nose
Pointing right down at the floor
Hey girl, your suspender shows
And the girl behind you looks a bit unsure

Round and round she goes
Little Miss Amanda Jones
I said round and round and round and round
To the balls and dinners and shows
The little girl she just wonders about
Till it's time for her coming out
Miss Amanda Jones

Miss You

Sometimes what I want to say to myself Sometimes I say Hoo hoo
hoo hoo hoo hoo hoo hoo hoo hoo hoo hoo hoo — hoo —
— hoo hoo hoo hoo — 1. Hoo hoo
I guess I'm ly-ing to my-self,— It's just
you and no-one else,— Lord I won't miss you child,—
You've just been
blot-ting out — my mind — fool-ing on my
time, No I won't miss you ba-by, _____
— Lord — I miss your touch,
Oh ooh _____ Ha ha
ha ha ha-ha __ ha ha ha ha ha-ha __
— ha ha ha ha __ ha ha.

Repeat ad lib and Fade

Monkey Man

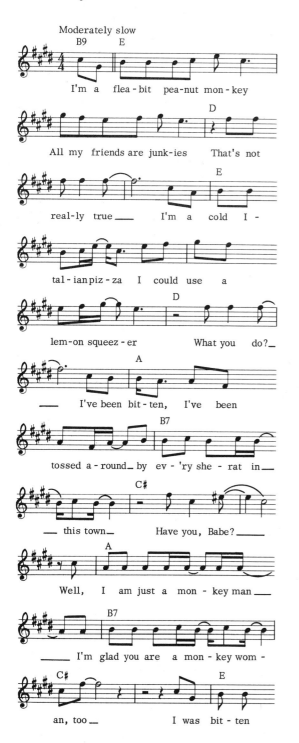

I'm a   mon - key ___

I'm a

Repeat and fade

Moonlight Mile

Slow tempo

mile _____ on down ___ the road _____

_ On down the road _____ down the road _____

_____ Yeah _____

Made a rag pile of my shiny clothes
Gonna warm my bones, gonna warm my bones
I got silence on my radio
Let the air waves flow, let the air waves flow
For I am sleeping under strange strange skies
Just another mad mad day on the road
My dreams is fading down the railway lines
I'm just about a moonlight mile on down the road

Mother's Little Helper

Things are different today, I hear ev'ry mother say
Cooking fresh food for a husband's just a drag
So she buys an instant cake, and she burns her frozen
  steak
And goes running for the shelter of a mother's little
  helper
And to help her on her way, get her through her busy
  day

Chorus:

Men just aren't the same today, I hear ev'ry mother
  say
They just don't appreciate that you get tired
They're so hard to satisfy, you can tranquilize your
  mind
So go running for the shelter of a mother's little
  helper
And to help you through the night, help to minimize
  your plight

Chorus:

Life's just much too hard today, I hear ev'ry mother
  say
The pursuit of happiness just seems a bore
And if you take more of those, you will get an over-
  dose
No more running to the shelter of a mother's little
  helper
They just helped you on your way through your busy
  dying day

Chorus:

My Obsession

Moderate, with a beat

My ob-ses-sions are your pos-ses-

sions Ev-'ry piece that I can get____

My ob-ses-sions are

your pos-ses-sions 'Til my mouth is

soak-ing wet____ I think_ I

blew it by_ con-fes-sion____

You can't dodge it

it's sim-ple log-ic You would be

bet-ter off with me____ And you'll

know it when you've lost it

lone-ly____

My obsession is your possession
Are you smiling in my way
My obsession is your possession
One that you should give away
Give it to me now I've no objection
I don't mind if it's unkind
And it's not my property
But I want it just to be mine
Exclusively

My obsession is your possession
Are you used to the idea?
My obsession is your possession
Do you feel at home right here?
You should relax is my impression
Didn't see you were so young
You need teaching you're a girl
I could almost be your son
There are things in this world
Please turn in my direction
That need teaching with discretion
No objection
My profession

19th Nervous Breakdown

When you were a child you were treated kind but never brought up right
You were overspoilt with a thousand toys and still you cried all night
Your mother who neglected you owes a million dollars tax
Your father's still perfecting ways of making sealing wax

You better stop, look around
Here it comes, here it comes, here it comes, here it
    comes,
Here it comes, your nineteenth nervous breakdown

Chorus:

You were still in school when you had that fool who
    really messed your mind
And after that you turned your back on treating people
    kind
On our first trip I tried so hard to rearrange your
    mind
But after a while I realised you were disarranging
    mine
You better stop, look around
Here it comes, here it comes, here it comes, here it
    comes,
Here it comes, your nineteenth nervous breakdown

Chorus:

No Expectations

Take me to_ the sta-tion_ and put me on_ a train_ I've got no ex-pec-ta-tions_ to pass through here a-gain

1. Once I was_ a rich_man_ and now I am_ so poor_ But nev-er in_ my sweet_ short life_ have I felt like_ this be-fore_

2. Your _ 3. Our love was like_ the wa-ter_ that splash-es on_ a stone_ Our love is like_

our mu-sic_ it's here and then it's gone_ 4. So

Hum _

Your heart is like a diamond
You throw your pearls at swine
And as I watched you leaving me
You packed my peace of mind

So take me to the airport
And put me on a plane
I've got no expectations
To pass through here again

94

Now I've Got A Witness

95

Off The Hook

Moderate beat

Sit-tin' in my bed-room late last night __

Got __ in-to bed and turned out the

light __ De-cide to call my

ba-by on the tel - e-phone __

All __ I got was a bus-y tone: _ It's off the

hook It's off the hook

It's off the hook It's off the

hook It's off the hook

hook It's off the hook It's off the

Repeat and fade

Off it so long she upset my mind
Why is she talkin' such a long time
Maybe she's a sleepin' maybe she's ill
Phone's disconnected unpaid bill

Chorus:

Don't wanna see her 'fraid of what I'd find
Tired of letting her upset me all the time
Back into bed started readin' my book
Take my phone right off the hook

Chorus:

96

On With The Show

Slowly

Good eve-ning one and all __ We're

all so glad to see you here _ We'll play your

fav-'rite songs _ while you all soak up the

at-mos-phere __ We'll start with

Old Man Riv - er Then may-be Storm-y Weath-er

too I'm sure you know_ just what to do

On with the show good health to you __

Please pour another glass
It's time to watch the cabaret
Your wife will never know
That you're not really working late
Your hostess here is Wendy
You'll find her very friendly, too
And we don't care just what you do
On with the show, good health to you

And if by chance you find
That you can't make it anymore
We'll put you in a cab
And get you safely to the door
Oh, we've got all the answers
And we've got lovely dancers, too
There's nothing else you have to do
On with the show, good health to you

You're all such lovely people
Dancing gaily round the floor
But if you have to fight, please
Take your troubles out the door
And now I say with sorrow
Until this time tomorrow, oh
We'll bid you all a fond adieu
On with the show, good health to you

97

100 Years Ago

Went out walking through the woods the other day
Can't you see the furrows in my forehead
What tender days we had, no secrets hid away
Now it seems about a hundred years ago
Now if you see me drinking bad red wine
Don't worry about this man that you love
Don't you think it's sometimes wise not to grow up?

One More Try

Repeat and fade

You've got a girl that doesn't think at all, she cries
The days and all the nights you try to satisfy
You bring her all the things she wants she don't
    improve
You think you'll give her up and tell her maybe I'll
    move

Sit down shut up don't dare cry
Things'll get better if you really try
So don't you panic, don't you panic give it one more
    try
So don't you panic, don't you panic give it one more
    try

Things don't matter easy come and go
And the thing that satisfies only time will show
You've got to know well what you want in your mind
'Cause it's better when you get it if you give it a try

Sit down shut up don't dare cry
Things'll get better if you really try
So don't you panic, don't you panic give it one more
    try
So don't you panic, don't you panic give it one more
    try

99

Out Of Time

A girl who wants to run away
Discovers that she's had her day
It's no good you thinking
That you are still mine
You're out of touch my baby
My poor unfaithful baby
I said baby, baby
You're out of time

Chorus:

You thought you were a clever girl
Giving up your social whirl
But you can't come back
And be the first in line
You're obsolete my baby
My poor old-fashioned baby
I said baby, baby
You're out of time

Chorus:

Paint It Black

I see a line of cars and they're all painted black
With flowers and my love both never to come back
I see people turn their heads and quickly look away
Like a new born baby it just happens ev'ry day

I look inside myself and see my heart is black
I see my red door and I want it painted black
Maybe then I'll fade away and not have to face the facts
It's not easy facing up when your whole world is black

No more will my green sea go turn a deeper blue
I could not foresee this thing happening to you
If I look hard enough into the setting sun
My love will laugh with me before the morning comes

I see a red door and I want it painted black
No colours anymore I want them to turn black.
I see the girls walk by dressed in their summer
    clothes
I have to turn my head until my darkness goes

101

Parachute Woman

Repeat and fade

Play With Fire

Em7
Well, you've got your dia - monds And you've

got your pret-ty clothes And the

chauf-feur drives your car You let

ev - 'ry - bod - y know But don't

G D G   C
play with me 'Cause you're play-ing with

Em7   *Fine*
fire ____   Your

Your mother she's an heiress
Owns a block in Saint John's Wood
And your father'd be there with her
If he only could
But don't play with me.... etc....

Your old man took her diamonds
And tiaras by the score
Now she gets her kicks in Stepney
Not in Knightsbridge anymore
So don't play with me.... etc....

Now you've got some diamonds
And you will have some others
But you'd better watch your step, girl
Or start living with your mother
So don't play with me.... etc....

103

Please Go Home

Repeat and fade

I don't want to be on my own
I can't talk much better alone
But I don't have to ring like a phone
Please go home

In some early part of your days
You were told of the devious ways
That you thought you could get without pay
Please go home

You reach a state of your mind
Where it's madness to look and to find
Your false affections though kind
Please go home

104

Respectable

of my life, — go take my wife,

— don't come back. —

1. (Instr) —
-pec - ta - ble, — she's so res-

-pec - ta - ble, — she's so de-

-lec - ta - ble, — she's so res-

-pec - ta - ble. — Get out —

— of my life — go take my wife. —

— don't come back — She's so res-

Get out — of my life, —

go take my wife, — don't come back.

Get out —

— Come back — Wow —

Ride On, Baby

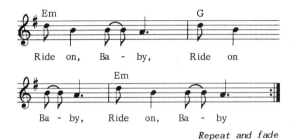

Ride on, Ba - by,   Ride on

Ba - by,   Ride on,   Ba - by

Repeat and fade

You walked up to me tryin' to look so shy
But the red round your eye
Shows that you ain't a child
Ride on baby, ride on baby
Ride on baby, ride on baby
I've seen your face in a trashy magazine
You know where you're going
But I don't like the places you've been

Ride on baby, ride on baby
Ride on baby, ride on baby
I can pick your face out from the front or behind
You may've looked pretty
But I can't say the same for your mind

Laugh up a bit more go on give it a try
If I'm not impressed
Well you can still cry
Ride on baby, ride on baby
Ride on baby, ride on baby
By the time you're thirty you'll look sixty-five
You won't look pretty
But your friends will have kissed you goodbye

Rip This Joint

Dal - las, Tex - as with the But - ter Queen.

Rip this joint, gon - na rip yours too, some

brand new steps and some weight to lose. Gon - na

roll this joint, gon - na get down low, so

round and round and round we'll go.

Wham, Bham, Bir - ming - ham,

Al - a - bam' don't give a damn.

Lit - tle Rock fit to drop.

Ah, let it rock.

107

Rocks Off

I hear you talking when I'm on the street
Your mouth don't move but I can hear you speak
What's the matter with the boy?
He don't come around no more
Is he checking out for sure?
Is he gonna close the door — on me?

I'm always hearing voices on the street
I want to shout but I can't hardly speak
I was making love last night
To a dancer friend of mine
I can't seem to stay in step
Cause she comes every time
That she pirouettes — over me

But I only get my rocks off while I'm dreaming
I only get my rocks off while I'm sleeping

I'm zipping through the days
At lightning speed
Plug in, flush out and fight the lucky feed
Heading for the overload
Splattered on the dusty road
Kick me like you've kicked before
I can't even feel the pain no more

But I only get my rocks of while I'm dreaming
I only get my rocks off while I'm sleeping

Feel so hypnotized can't describe the scene
Feel so mesmerized all that inside me
The sunshine bores the daylight out of me
Chasing shadows moonlight mystery

Headed for the overload
Splattered on the dusty road
Kick me like you've kicked before
I can't even feel the pain no more

But I only get my rocks off while I'm dreaming
I only get my rocks off while I'm sleeping

Ruby Tuesday

Don't question why she needs to be so free
She'll tell you it's the only way to be
She just can't be chained to a life where nothing's
    gained
And nothing's lost at such a cost

Chorus:

There's no time to lose I heard her say
Cash your dreams before they slip away
Dying all the time lose your dreams and you
Will lose your mind ain't life unkind

Chorus:

109

Sad Day

110

(I Can't Get No) Satisfaction

Repeat and fade

Shattered

She Smiled Sweetly

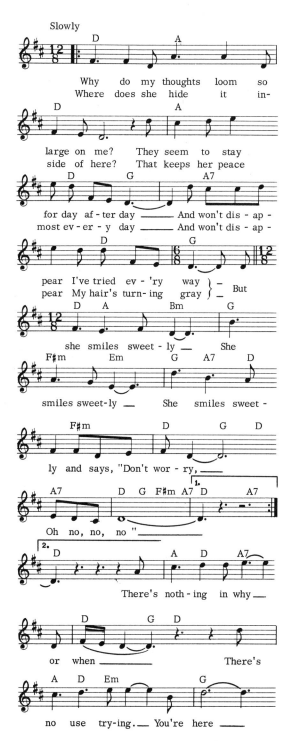

She's A Rainbow

Have you seen her all in gold?
Like a queen in days of old
She shoots colours all around
Like a sunset going down
Have you seen a lady fairer?

She comes in colours ev'rywhere
She combs her hair
She's like a rainbow
Combing colours in the air ev'rywhere
She comes in colours

114

Shine A Light

Saw you stretched out in room ten-o-nine with a
smile on your face and a tear right in your eye.
Couldn't see to get a line on you,
my sweet hon-ey love. Ber-ber jew-'lry
jan-gling down the streets make you shut your
eyes at ev-'ry wo-man that you meet
could not seem to get a high on you,
my sweet hon-ey love.
May the good Lord shine a light on you,
Make ev-e-ry song your fa-vor-ite tune.
May the good Lord shine a light on you,
warm like the eve-ning sun, Well you're

D.C. to Fade

Fade x 2

Drunk in the alley baby with your clothes all torn
And your late night friends leave you in the cold grey dawn.
Just seemed too many flies on you,
I just can't brush them off.

Angels beating all their wings in time,
With smiles on their faces and a gleam right in their eyes,
Thought I heard one sigh for you,
Come on up, come on up, now, come on up now.

May the good Lord shine a light on you,
Make every song you sing your favorite tune.
Make the good Lord shine a light on you,
Warm like the evening sun.

115

Short And Curlies

Too bad She's got you by the
boards you can't get free at all She's got your
name she's got your num-ber You're scream
-ing like thun-der and you
can't get a-way from it all It's too bad
she grabbed a hand-ful and you
can't get a-way from it all. It's too bad
all. and you can't get a-way from it

It's too bad She's got you by the boards
You can't get free at all
She's got your name she's got your number
You're screaming like thunder and you can't get away from it all
It's too bad she grabbed a handful and you can't get away from it all
It's too bad

It's too bad She's got you by the boards
She's nailed you to the wall
Oh it's a shame but it's funny
She's crashed your car she's spent your money but,
You can't get away from it all
It's too bad and ooh it's painful and you can't break away from this

116
Silver Train

Sing This Altogether
(See What Happens)

Moderate tempo

Why don't we sing_ this song all to-geth - er? O-pen our heads_ Let the pic-tures come_____ And if we close_ all our eyes to-geth - er Then we will see_ where we all come from _____

Why don't we sing_ the song all to-geth - er? O-pen our minds_ let the pic-tures come ____ And if we close_ all our eyes to-geth-er Then we will see_ where we all come from _____

Pic - tures of us thru_____ the steam - y haze _____
Pic - tures of us beat - ing on__ our drums _____
Pic - tures of us spin_____ the cir - cling sun

Pic - tures of us paint - ed on__ our caves _____
Nev - er stop-ping till ____ the rain has come _____
Pic - tures of us show_____ that we're all one _____

Sister Morphine

Slowly (24 bars per minute)

this shot   will be in the line __

sit a-round __ and watch ___ and mean-while

the sheets stain red __

(Orch.)

The scream of the ambulance is soundin' in my ear
Tell me, Sister Morphine, how long have I been lyin'
      here?
What am I doing in this place?
Why does the doctor have no face?
Oh, I can't crawl across the floor
Can't you see, Sister Morphine, I'm just trying to
      score.

And that just goes to show things are not what they
      seem.
Please, Sister Morphine, turn my nightmare into
      dream.
Oh, can't sleep till I'm feeling fine
And that this shot will be in the line

Please, Cousin Cocaine, lay your cool hands on my
      head
Hey, Sister Morphine, you just make her like dead
For you know between the night time and the morning
      of the day
That you sit around and watch and meanwhile the
      sheets stain red

Sittin' On A Fence

All of my friends at school grew up and settled down
Then they mortgaged up their lives
When things got set too much but I think it's true
They just get married 'cause they've nothing else to do
Chorus:
The day can come when you get old and sick and tired
  of life
You just never realise
May be the choice you made wasn't really right
But you've got her and you don't come back at night
Chorus:

120

Some Girls

French girls they want Cartier, Italian girls want cars,
American girls want everything in the world you can possibly imagine.
English girls, they're so pretty – I can't stand them on the telephone
Sometimes I take the receiver off the hook, I don't want them to ever
    call at all.
White girls they're pretty funny, but sometimes they drive me mad
Black girls just like to get fucked all night; I just don't have that much
    jam.
Chinese girls, they're so gentle – they're really such a tease
You never know quite what they're cookin' inside those silky sleeves.
Give me all your money, give me all your gold
I'll give ya a house back in Zuma Beach and give you half of what I
    owe.
Some girls they're so pure, some girls so corrupt
Some girls give me children I only made love to once
So give me half your money, give me half your car
Give me half of everything – I'll make you the world's greatest star
    by half.
So give me all your money, give me all your gold
Let's go back to Zuma Beach – I'll give you half of everything I owe.

121

Some Things Just Stick In Your Mind

Why does the sky turn grey ev-'ry night?
Sun-rise a-gain in sight.
Why do you think of the first girl you met? Some things just stick in your mind.

Why does the rain fall down on the earth?
Why do the clouds keep cryin'?
Why do you seek her love like a child?
Some things just stick in your mind.

Why, when the children grow up and leave
Still remember their nursery rhymes?
Why must there be so much pain in their lives?
Some things just stick in their minds.

122

Something Happened To Me Yesterday

Some-thing hap-pened to me yes-ter-day — Some-thing I can't speak of right a-way — Some-thing hap-pened to me — Some-thing, oh so groov-y — Some-thing hap-pened to me yes-ter-day — He don't know if it's right or wrong — May-be he should tell some-one — He's not sure just what it was — Or if it's a-gainst the law — Some-thing —

Something very strange I hear you say
You're talking in a most peculiar way
But something really threw me
Something oh so groovy
Something happened to me yesterday

He don't know just where it's gone
He don't really care at all
No one's sure just what it was
Or the meaning and the cause
Something . . . .

He don't know if it's right or wrong
Maybe he should tell someone
He's not sure just what it was
Or if it's against the law
Something . . . .

Someone says there's something more to pay
For sins that you committed yesterday
Is really rather drippy
But something oh so trippy
Something . . . .

He don't know just where it's gone
He don't really care at all
No one's sure just what it was
Or the meaning and the cause
Something . . . .

Someone's singing loud across the bay
Sitting on a mat about to pray
Isn't half as loony
As something oh so groovy
Something . . . .

123

Soul Survivor

con - fi - dence sags, _____ you got me

pack-ing my bags. _____ I'll stow-a-

- way at sea, _____ you make me

mu - ti - ny, _____ where you are _____ I

_____ won't be, _____ you're gonna be the death of me. _____

Star Star

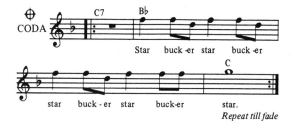

Honey: honey call me on the telephone
I know you are moving out to Hollywood with your can of tasty foam
All those beat up friends of mine
Got to get them in my book
And lead guitars and movie stars, get their toes beneath my hook
Yeah you were starbucker, starbucker star
Starbucker, starbucker star
Starbucker, starbucker star

Yes I heard about your polaroids now that's what I call obscene
Your tricks with fruit were kinda cute
Now that really is a scene
Honey I miss your two tone kisses, legs wrapped around me tight
If ever I get back to New York
I'm gonna make you scream all night
Yeah starbucker, starbucker star
Starbucker, starbucker star
Starbucker, starbucker star.

At the draw I got mad at you for giving it to Steve McQueen
And you and me made a pretty pair falling through the silver screen
Now baby I am open to anything I don't know where to draw the line
Well I am making bets that you gonna get your man before he dies
You were starbucker, starbucker, starbucker star
Were starbucker, starbucker, starbucker star
Were starbucker, starbucker, starbucker star
Were starbucker, starbucker, starbucker star

125

Stoned

126

Stop Breaking Down

Moderate Rock

Ev-'ry time I'm walking all down the street,— some pret-ty ma-ma start break-ing down on me. Stop break-ing down.— Ba - by please stop break - ing down,— Stuff is gonna bust your brains out ba-by. Gon-na make you lose your mind.

You Saturday night women
Now you just ape and clown,
You don't do nothing
But tear my reputation down.
Stop breaking down.
Mama please stop breaking down.
Stuff is gonna bust your brains out baby.
Gonna make you lose your mind.

I love my baby ninety nine degrees,
But that mama got a pistol,
Laid it down on me.
Stop breaking down,
Mama please stop breaking down.
Stuff is gonna bust your brains out baby.
Gonna make you lose your mind.

Stray Cat Blues

yeah, you're a strange stray cat Oh yeah,—

— don't scream like that— Bet your

ma-ma don't know you scratch like that—

D7(sus4)   D7
Bet she don't know you can bite like that—

D7   C   G
You say you got a friend, she's wild-er than

G   D7   C
you — Well, why don't you bring her up-

G   D7   C
stairs If she's so wild   she can

G   A7(sus4)
join in too— But it's no hang-ing

mat-ter— it's no cap-i-tal crime—

A7   C   G
— Oh yeah, you're a strange stray

cat Oh yeah,— don't scratch like that.—

D7   G
Oh yeah,—— you're a strange stray

cat — Bet you're ma-ma don't know you

D7   D7(sus4)
bite like that— I bet she nev-er saw you

D7   D7 (Orch.)
scratch my back—

Repeat and fade

Street Fighting Man

Moderate Rock

Stupid Girl

I'm not talking about the way she digs for gold
Look at that stupid girl
Well I'm talking about the way she grabs and holds
Look at that stupid girl
The way she talks about someone else
That she don't even know herself
She the sickest thing in this world
Look at that stupid girl

Well I'm sick and tired
And I really have my doubts
I've tried and tried
But it never really works out
Like a lady in waiting to a virgin queen
Look at that stupid girl
She bitches about things that she's never seen
Look at that stupid girl
It doesn't matter if she dyes her hair
Or the colour of the shoes she wears
She the worst thing in this world
Look at that stupid girl

Like a lady in waiting to a virgin queen
Look at that stupid girl
She bitches about things that she's never seen
Look at that stupid girl
She purrs like a pussy cat
Then she turns round and hisses back
She the sickest thing in this world
Look at that stupid girl

130

Surprise Surprise

Why did you have to
Go and fool after
We had got along so fine
But surprise, surprise
Surprise, surprise
Ain't nothin' strange to me
'Cos I knew you was tellin' lies
Knew you was tellin' lies
I could see it in your eyes

I hope you're tired of
All your chasin' round
Thinkin' I'm alone all night
But surprise, surprise
Surprise, surprise
You're only fooling yourself
Knew you was tellin' lies
I could see it in your eyes

Moderately bright

Well, I told friends of mine —

You been tell-in' lies —

How I was wrapped up in you

But, sur-prise,— sur-prise —

Sur-prise,— sur-prise —

I nev-er want-ed you that bad —

'Cause I knew— you was

tell-in' lies— Knew— you was

tell-in' lies — I could see it

in your eyes eyes —

131
Sway

Repeat and fade

Sweet Black Angel

133

Sweet Virginia

Thank you for your wine,
California,
Thank you for your sweet and bitter fruits.
Yes, I got the desert in my toenail
And I hid the 'speed' inside my shoe.

Sympathy For The Devil

hope you guess my name ____

But what's puz-zling you__ is the na -

ture of my game____ Just as

ev-'ry cop__ is a crim-i-nal And

all the sin-ners Saints__ As heads

is tails,__ just call me Lu-ci-fer

'Cause I'm in need of some re-straint__

____ So if you meet me, have some

cour-te-sy__ Have some sym-pa-thy

and some taste Use all__ your well __

____ learned pol-i-tesse Or I'll lay your

soul to waste! Pleased to meet

you hope you guess my name _____

____ But what's puz-zling you __ is the

na-ture of my game _____

2nd Chorus:

Pleased to meet you, hope you guess my name
But what's puzzling you is the nature of my game

I watched with glee while your kings and queens
Fought for ten decades for the Gods they made
I shouted out, 'Who killed the Kennedy's?'
When after all it was you and me

So let me please introduce myself
I am a man of wealth and taste
And I lay traps for troubadours
Who get killed before they reach Bombay

2,000 Light Years From Home

Moderately, with a beat

Sun turn - ing 'round with grace-ful mo - tion We're set - ting off with soft ex - plo - sion Bound for a star with fi - ery o - ceans It's so ver - y lone - ly You're a hun - dred light years from home Freez-ing red des - erts turn to dark En - er - gy in ev - er - y part

It's so ver - y lone - ly
It's so ver - y lone - ly

You're six hun - dred
You're one thou - sand light years from home

Bell flight four - teen you now can land See you on Al - der - Bo - ran Safe on the green des - ert sand It's so ver - y lone - ly You're two thou-sand light years from home

Repeat and fade

136

2,000 Man

2120 South Michigan Avenue

Take It Or Leave It

Moderate tempo

You can turn off and on more

times Than a flash-ing ne - on sign

when you want You're bad, but you

can be so kind Refrain: Just take it

or leave it Don't tell your

friends just what you're gon - na do now

You take it, or leave it

It's just my life

1. There've been 2. Oo la la

la, ta ta ta ta, La la la la _ Oo la la

la la, ta ta ta, La la ____ Oo la la

la la ta ta ta La la la la _ Oo la la

la, ta ta ta ta, La la I'm sick and....

life ____ Oo la la

la, ta ta ta ta, La la la la _ Oo la la

la, ta ta ta ta, La la ____ Oo la la

D.S. %

There've been times when you try making eyes
At all my so called friends then you go
Now you're back, but you can be so kind

Refrain:

I'm sick and tired of the smile that you give
When you don't come home at night you said you'd
 called
That's a lie, but you can be so kind

Refrain:

139

Tell Me

I wait as the days go by
I long for the nights to go by
I hear the knock on my door
That never comes
I hear the telephone
That hasn't rung

Chorus

You said we're through before
You walked out on me before
I tried tell you but you didn't want to know
This time you're diff'rent and determined to go

Chorus

140

The Lantern

You cross the sea of night
Free from the spell of flight,
The cloak you wear is a spirit shroud
You'll wake me in my sleeping hours,
Like a cloud, so
Please carry the lantern high

Me, in my sorry plight
You, waiting every night
My face, it turns a deathly pale
You're talking to me through your veil
I hear you wail
Please carry the lantern high

The servants sleep, the door is barred,
You hear the stopping of my heart
We never part, so
Please carry the lantern high

141

(This Could Be) The Last Time

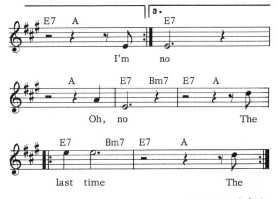

Repeat and fade

I'm sorry girl but I can't stay
Feeling like I do today
Staying here is too much sorrow
Guess I'll feel the same tomorrow

Well this could be the last time
This could be the last time
Maybe the last time
I don't know
Oh no

I've told you once and I've told you twice
Someone'll have to pay the price
Here's the chance to change your mind
I'll be gone a long time

Well this could be the last time
This could be the last time
Maybe the last time
I don't know
Oh no

The Salt Of The Earth

hard-work-ing peo - ple   Let's drink

to the salt of the earth —   Let's

think of the two thou - sand mil - lion

Let's   thínk   of   the

hum - ble   of   birth _____

Repeat and fade

Raise your glass to the hard working people
Let's drink to the uncounted heads
Let's think of the wavering millions
Who need leaders but get gamblers instead

Spare a thought for the stay-at-home voter
His empty eyes gaze at strange beauty shows
And a parade of gray suited grafters
A choice of cancer or polio

The Singer, Not The Song

The same old places and the same old song
We've been going there for much too long
There's something wrong
And it gives me that feeling inside
That I know I must be right
It's the singer, not the song

The Spider And The Fly

She was coming flirty
She look'd about thirty
I would have run away, but I was on my own
She told me later she's a machine operator
She said she liked the way I held the microphone
I said My! My! like a spider to a fly
Jump right ahead in my web!

145

The Under Assistant West Coast Promotion Man

Moderate tempo

Well, I'm wait - ing at the bus stop

in down - town L. A.

Well, I'm wait - ing at the bus stop

in down - town L. A.

Well, I'd much rath - er be on a bird

walk on Broad - way

Well, I'm sit - ting here think - ing just

how sharp I am

Well, I'm sit - ting here think - ing just

how sharp I am

I'm an un - der as - sist - ant West

Coast pro - mo man

1.

2. Well, I pro -

Well, promo groups when they come into town
Well, promo groups when they come into town
Well, they laugh at my toupe they sure put me down

Well, I'm sitting here thinking just how sharp I am
Well, I'm sitting here thinking just how sharp I am
I'm a necessary talent behind ev'ry rock 'n' roll band

146

Think

fault was that ____ then?

Tell me whose fault was that ____ then?

Last time repeat from
* ad lib. and fade

Think about a year ago
How we lived I'll never know
Conning people for a small dime
Here's another piece of my mind

Chorus:

Changes may have come too fast
But I thought we'll always last
Situations may have changed
But I think we're still the same

Chorus:

We're not children any more
We don't need to play with toys
Take a look and you will surely find
You're getting much too old before your time

Chorus:

Through The Lonely Nights

Verse

Through the lone - ly nights _____ I

think of you _____ through the lone - ly

ho - urs _ I dream of you, _____

I _ don't know why _____ I do _ it

but I do, _____ why _____ do you

take it _ what's wrong with you? _____

Ev - 'ry time I

see ya, Ev - 'ry time I see 'ya

Ev - 'ry time I see ya Ev - 'ry time I

see _ you

CODA Vocals ad. lib. To Fade

With the lonely weekends I'm far from you,
Why you're coming on, like you're supposed to do?
Oh but you know me so well,
And your time ain't so hard to sell.

In your cherry dresses and your shiny shoes
In a doorway on some neon walk
Making the lonely pay for me
Why don't we set each other free.

When did I mislead ya
When did I mistreat ya
When did I mistreat ya
When did I deceive ya

Till The Next Goodbye

A movie house on Forty second street
Ain't a very likely place for you and I to meet
Watching the snow swirl around your hair
and round your feet
And I'm thinking to myself you surely look a treat

You give me a cure all from New Orleans
Now that's a recipe I sure do need
Some cider vinegar and some elderberry wine
May cure all your ills but it can't cure mine

Time Waits For No One

Time can tear down a building
Or destroy a woman's face
Hours are like diamonds
Don't let them waste
And time waits for no man
No favours has he
And time waits for no one
And it won't wait for me
Oh la la la la la la la la la la la la la

Men they build towers to their passing,
Yeah to their fame everlasting
Here he comes chopping and reaping
Hear him laugh at their cheating
And time waits for no man
And it won't wait for me
Yes time waits for no one
And it won't wait for me

Drink in your summer
Gather your corn
The dreams of the night-time
Will vanish by dawn
And time waits for no one
And it won't wait for me
Time waits for no one and won't wait for me.

150

Torn And Frayed

let it steal your heart a-

way, let it steal your heart a-

-way. Well his

151

Try A Little Harder

Don't you wor-ry try a lit-tle hard-er

Don't you wor-ry try a lit-tle hard-er,

Don't you wor-ry try a lit-tle hard-er,

Don't you wor-ry try a lit-tle hard-er, The

girl rea-lly wants you man Don't you see you got-ta

give her all the lov-in' that she needs,

have a try Try it one more

time have a try Try it one more

time time Try a lit-tle bit

hard-er Try a lit-tle bit hard-er. Try a

lit-tle bit hard-er If you're

with your ba-by when the day turns to night, You're

got to give her lov-in', make her feel al-right

have a try.

Don't you worry try a little harder,
Don't you worry try a little harder,
Give her loving that's a little stronger,
Give her loving that's a little stronger,
If you're with your baby when the day turns to night
You've got to give her lovin' make her feel alright
It's alright
It's alright
Try one more time
It's alright

Don't you worry, try a little harder,
Don't you worry, try a little harder,
Say goodnight but stay a little longer,
Say goodnight but stay a little longer,
You've got to keep her from crying and you've gotta try
To work very hard to keep her satisfied
Just try
Try it one more time
Try it one more time
Have a try

152

Tumbling Dice

roll ____ me and call me the tum - blin', ____

roll ____ me and call me the tum - blin'

(Got to

dice. ____ Got to
roll me,)

roll me, got to

153

Turd On The Run

Grabbed hold of your coat - tail but it

come off in my hand, ____ I

reached for your la - pel ____ but it

weren't sewn on so grand. ____

Begged, prom-ised an - y - thing if

on - ly you would stay, ____ well, I

lost a lot of love ____ o - ver you.

7

Fell down to my knees ____ and I

hung on - to your pants, ____ but

you just kept on run-nin' while they

ripped off in my hands.

Di - 'mond rings, vas - e - line, ____

you give me dis - ease, ____ well, I

lost a lot of love ____ o - ver you. ____

5

I boo - gied in ____ the ball

- room, I boo - gied in ____ the dark;

Tie your hands,

tie your feet, throw you to the sharks.

____ Make you sweat, make you scream,

make you wish, you'd nev - er been, I

lost a lot of love ____ o - ver you,

Under My Thumb

Under my thumb her eyes are just kept to herself
Under my thumb well I can still look at someone else
It's down to me, the way she talks when she's spoken
    to
It's down to me, the change has come, she's under
    my thumb

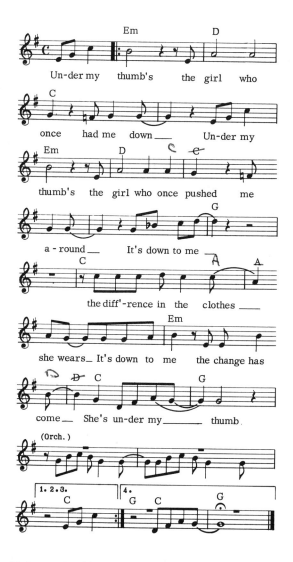

Un-der my thumb's the girl who
once had me down ___ Un-der my
thumb's the girl who once pushed me
a - round ___ It's down to me
the diff'-rence in the clothes ___
she wears ___ It's down to me the change has
come ___ She's un-der my ___ thumb.

(Orch.)

1. 2. 3.   4.

Under my thumb's a squirming dog who's just had her
    day
Under my thumb's a girl who has just changed her
    ways
It's down to me, the way she does just what she's told
It's down to me, the change has come, she's under
    my thumb

Under my thumb's a siamese cat of a girl
Under my thumb she's the sweetest pet in the world
It's down to me, she does just what she's told
It's down to me, the change has come, she's under
    my thumb

155

Ventilator Blues

(Walking Thru The) Sleepy City

When you walk thru the sleepy city
In the night it looks so pretty
Tired of walking on my own
It looks better when you're not alone

We Love You

With excitement

Cm   **G**

We _____ love you _____
We _____ love 'they' _____

Cm   **F**

We _____ love you _____ And we
We _____ love 'they' _____ And we

D   **F**   **C**

hope that you will love 'we',
want you to love 'they',

G   **G**

too _____
too _____   Ah _____

A7   **D**

we   just came

G   **D**

to hound 'we'_ and love is all a-round 'we'_

G   **D**   **A**

Love can't get our minds off _ We love you, we

1. **G6** **D**   **2.** **A7**   **D**

love you   love you _____ Ah, _____

A7   **D**

_____ we love you _____ Ah, _____

G

_____ we love you _____ And we

E   **F**   **C**   **G**

hope that you will love 'we', too _____

A7

_____ We love you _____ We love you _

_____ We love you _____ We

Repeat and fade

158

We're Wasting Time

We're wasting time inside my mind
The thought of you won't go away come every day
We're just wasting time.

We're wasting time
My clothes are fine
Still fresh and clean
The sweet perfume in our balloon
We're just wasting time.

With that face that I've seen
Maybe thinks the same as me
Well there is nothing that we're learning
While her hands keep turning
Oh girl! Oh girl! Can't you see
We're just wasting time.

Wasting time inside my mind
The thought of you won't go away come every day
We're just wasting time.

We're wasting time
My clothes are fine
Still fresh and clean
The sweet perfume in our balloon
We're just wasting time.

What A Shame

Moderate blues beat

What a shame __ noth-in' seems to be go-in' right What a shame __ noth-in' seems to be go-in' right It seems eas-y to me __ that ev-'ry-thing-'ll be all right __ What a

What a shame they always wanna start a fight
What a shame they always wanna start a fight
Well it scares me so I have to sleep in a shelter all
    night
What a shame y'all heard what I said
What a shame y'all heard what I said
You might wake up in the morning find you poor
    selves dead

160

What To Do

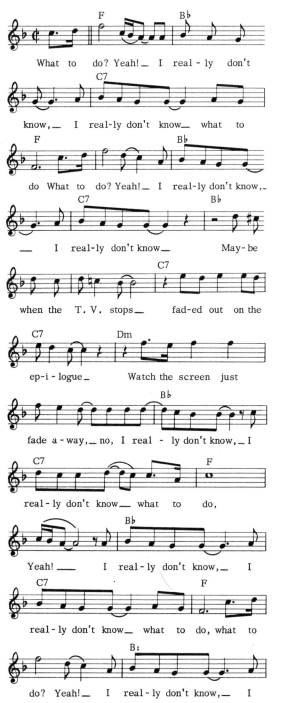

do what to do? Yeah! __ I real-ly don't

know, __ I real-ly don't know __

Hur-ry, peo-ple, get on your train __

don't be late for work a-gain __

I think it's time to go to bed __ no, I

real-ly don't know __ I real-ly don't

know __ what to do, Yeah!

When The Whip Comes Down

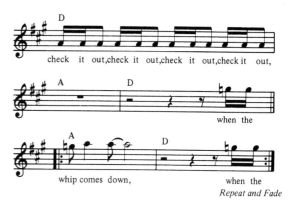

when the

check it out, check it out, check it out, check it out,

whip comes down,   when the

when the

whip comes down,   when the

whip comes down,   when the

Repeat and Fade

when the

whip comes down,   when the

whip comes   down,   I'll be

run -ning this   town,   when   the

shit hits the fan ____ I'll be   sit - ting on the

can   when the   whip comes down,

Watch out   ba-by, ____

check it out, check it out, check it out, check it out,

Who's Been Sleeping Here

Don't you look like, like a Goldilocks?
There must be somewhere, somewhere you can
    stop
There's the noseless old newsboy, the old
    British Brigadier
They'll tell me now who's been sleeping here

Who's been eating, eating off my plate?
Who will tell me, who'll investigate?
There's the sergeants, the soldiers, the cruel
    old grenadiers
They'll tell me now, who's been sleeping here

Repeat and fade

What'd you say, girl, who'd you see that night?
Oh I was doing something right
But the soldier, the sailor, and then there's the
    three musketeers
They'll tell me now, who's been sleeping here

163

Who's Driving Your Plane

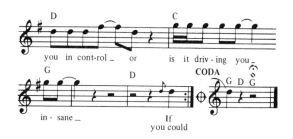

If I could wave a magic wand and maybe you'd change back to
being a blonde
And your skirt would come down and cover your feet.
If I said "it's not camp to have Tiffany lamps;"
You would throw them right out in the street.
And I wonder who's driving your plane (etc.)

You could stand on your head or maybe sing in your bed,
If I said it was the thing to do.
If you're in with the faces and their get away places,
They don't take no notice of you,
Cause the trendy pace setters will cause you pain,
'Cause they'll want to know who's driving your plane?

164

Wild Horses

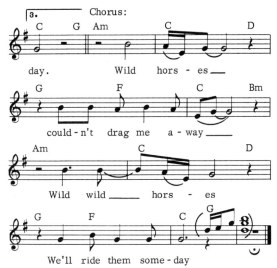

Slowly *(20 bars per minute)*

Child - hood liv - ing___

is eas - y to do___

The things_ you __ want - ed___

I bought_ them __ for you___

Grace - less la - dy___ you know___

___ who I am ___ You know__ I can't_

___ let __ you__ slide through my

Chorus:

hands ___ Wild hors - es___

could-n't drag me a - way ___

Wild, wild ___ hors - es

(1.2.) could-n't drag me a - way ___
(3.) we'll ride them some - day ___

Chorus:

day. Wild hors - es___

could - n't drag me a - way ___

Wild wild ___ hors - es

We'll ride them some - day

I watched you suffer a dull aching pain,
Now you've decided to show me the same
No sweeping exits or offstage lines
Could make me feel bitter or treat you unkind

I know I've dreamed you a sin and a lie
I have my freedom but I don't have much time
Faith has been broken, tears must be cried
Let's do some living after we die

165

Winter

And it sure has been a cold cold winter
And it ain't been blowing from the south
And it sure has been a cold cold winter.
And the light of love is all burned out
And it sure has been a cold cold winter
And my feet been draggin' 'cross the ground
And the fields has all been brown and barren
And springtime takes the long way around
And I wish I'd been out in Stony Canyon

Yesterday's Papers

Moderate with a beat

in the world

Living a life of constant change
Every day means a turn of a page
Yesterday's papers are such bad news
The same thing applies to me and you

Who wants yesterday's papers?
Who wants yesterday's girl?
Who wants yesterday's papers?
Nobody in the world

Seems very hard to have just one girl
When there's a million in the world
All of these people just can't wait
To fall right into their big mistake

'Cause who wants yesterday's papers?
Who wants yesterday's girl?
Who wants yesterday's papers?
Nobody in the world

You Can't Always Get What You Want

D.S. % al Verse 4.   Verse 4.

"dead"___ And you saw her to-day at___

___ the re-cep - tion__ In her glass

was a bleed-ing man__ She was prac-ticed

at the art___ of de-cep-tion__ I could

tell by her blood - stained ___

hands_____ *D.S. % al Fine* And you

You Got The Silver

You Gotta Move

Ha ah ha ha ha
Ha ha ha ha ha ha ha ha ha ha ha ha
Ah ha ha ha ha ha ha ha ha
You gotta move.

Ha ah ha ha, Ha ha ha
ha ha ha ha ha ha ha ha ha
Ah ha ha ha ha
ha ha ha ha ha you gotta move.

You see that woman who walks the street
You see that policeman upon his beat
But when the Lord gets ready
You gotta move
Ah ha ha.

Cocksucker Blues

Well, I asked a young policeman if he'd only lock me up
for the night.
Well, I've had pigs in the farmyard — some of them, some
of them are alright,
Well, he fucked me with his truncheon and his helmet was
way too tight.
Oh where can I get cock suck etc.

171

Dance

Summer Romance

Just a few days and you'll be back in your class,
Sucking up the teacher and tryin' to get an 'A' pass.
You're tryin' to hide your make up and you're tryin' to flash your legs,
No sympathy from your spotty friends.

Money so much, I need money so bad
And I can't be your mum, I don't wanna be your dad.
I'm a serious man, I got serious lusts,
Now I'll have to do away with the greasy kid stuff.

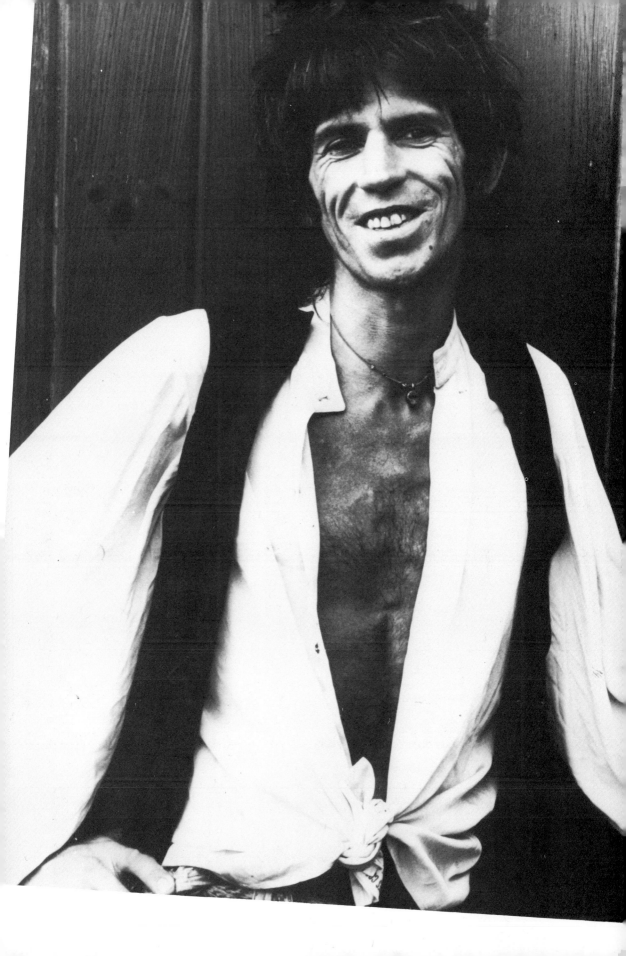

173

Send It To Me

I'm send-ing a let-ter to my

sis-ter In Aus-tra-li-a

Sis-ter it reads Ain't you got no

daugh-ter no sec-ond cou-sin,

that needs my lov-ing ___ Send it to me ___

___ Instr.

Send it to me
Send it to me
Send it to me
Send it to me.

She won't have to wash or scrape
She won't have to relocate
I guarantee her personal security.

She don't have to be five foot ten,
A blonde or a brunette,
She don't have to be no social hostess
Send her.

She might work in a factory
Right next door to me
In my fantasy
Send it to me.

Send it to me
Send it to me
Send it to me
Send it to me.

She could be a Roumanian
She could be a Bulgarian
She could be Albanian
She could be Hungarian.

She might be Ukranian
She could be Australian
She could be the Alien
Send it to be.

Send it to me. (to fade)

Let Me Go

Maybe I'll become a play-boy
Hang around in gay bars
And move to the west side of town.
You gonna get it straight from the shoulder
Can't you see the party's over,
Let me go, let me go.

So you think I'm giving you the brush-off
I'm just telling you to shove off
Hey! Please let me go.
This ain't the time to waste my breath
We're going into sudden death
Hey, Let me go.

Can't you get it through your thick head
This affair is dead as a do-do
The bell has rung and I've called time
The chair is on the table, (out the door baby)
Baby won't you let me go.

Let me go
Baby won't you let me go
Let me go
Baby won't you let me go
Let me go. (Rpt. *to fade*)

175

Indian Girl

Where The Boys Go

.dis - co Where the boys all go, where the boys all go.

CODA

Instrumental

Chorus. repeat ad lib.   to Fade

Hey you girls, what you doin' tonight?
Do you want a dance or do you want a fight.
Listen here darling I know the score,
Paint your face, dye your hair, I'll see you round the back;

177

Down In The Hole

Slow beat   Bm

Will all your mo·ney   buy you for -
None of your mo·ney   Will buy you for -

give - ness,   keep you from sick-ness
give - ness,   none of your jewel-ry

or keep you from cold.   Will all your
none of your gold.   Your blackmarket

mo·ney___   keep you from mad-ness,
ciga-rettes___   your American night-clubs

keep you from sad-ness   when you're
they've got no -

down in the hole___ 'cause you'll be down in the gut -
where left.   some thing for

Bm

ter,   you'll be beg - ging for
ter   you'll be beg - ging for
no - thing   oh all what your

G

cig - a - rettes,   bum-ming for
cig - a - rettes,   beg - ging for -
friends   got,   some-thing for

F#sus4   F#

ny-lons   in the A-mer - i - can zone___
give-ness,   I'll let you know___
noth-ing   yes that's all you know___

E   F#

You'll be   down   in the hole,___
You'll be   down   in the hole,___
There's some-thing down   in the hole,___

Bm   G

down in the hole ___
after dig-ging the trench-es
down in the hole,___

F#sus4   F#   to Coda

no es - cape from trouble   no-where to
look-ing for cov - er and finding that there is nowhere to
some - thing down   in the

| 1 E   F# | 2 E   F#   D.C. |

go.   Down in the gut-   go

CODA
E   Instrumental

hole   to fade

178

Emotional Rescue

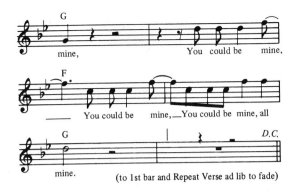

Ad Lib on Verse (5°)

Yes you could be mine, tonight and ev'ry night
I will be your knight in shining armour
Coming to your Emotional Rescue
(You will be mine, You will be mine, All mine) Rpt.
I will be your knight in shining armour,
Riding across the desert on a fine Arab charger.

179

She's So Cold

2 Yes I've tried rewiring her
I've tried refiring her
I think her engine is permanently stalled.
She's so cold, she's so cold,
She's so cold, cold, cold like a tomb-stone.
She's so cold, she's so cold.
She's so cold, cold, cold like an ice-cream cone.
She's so cold, she's so cold.
When I touch her my hand just froze.

3 I'm so hot for her, I'm so hot for her,
I'm so hot for her.
Put your hand on the heat, put your hand on the heat,
And come on baby, let's go.
She's so cold, she's so cold, cold,
She's so c-c-c-c-c-cold but she's a beautiful girl.

4 She's so cold, She's so cold,
I think she was born in the Arctic Zone
She's so cold, she's so cold,
When I touch her, my hand just froze.
She's so cold, she's goddam cold
She's so cold, cold, cold she's so cold.

5 Who would believe you were a beauty indeed
When the days get shorter and the nights get long,
When the light fades and the rain comes
No-body will know,
When you're old, when you're old,
Nobody will know that
you were a beauty,
A Sweet, sweet beauty,
A Sweet, sweet beauty, but stone, stone cold.
You're so cold, you're so cold, cold, cold,
You're so cold, you're so cold,
(ad lib. on Verse 1) to fade

All About You

Who'll tell me no lies
And let me think they're true
I heard one or two
And they weren't about me,
They weren't about her,
They were all about you.

I may miss you
But missing me just isn't you,
I'm so sick and tired of hanging around dogs.
Who'll tell me those lies,
And let me think they're true.
I heard one or two and they
Weren't about me,
Weren't about you,
They're all about you,
All about you.
So sick and tired,
What should I do,
You want,
You get
So how come I'm still in love with you?

The laughs may be cheap
That's just 'cause the joke's about you
I'm so sick and tired
Hanging around with dogs like you
You're the first to get laid
Always the last bitch to get paid

Index

Discography:
Supplement

Emotional Rescue

She's So Cold (Jagger, Richard)/**Send It To Me**
(Jagger, Richard)
Rolling Stones Records RSR 106.
Released: September, 1980
Produced: The Glimmer Twins.

Sucking In The Seventies

Rolling Stones Records CUNS 39112.
Released: April 20, 1981.
Produced: The Glimmer Twins.
Shattered (Jagger, Richards)/Everything Is Turning To
Gold (Jagger, Richards, Wood)/Hot Stuff (Jagger,
Richards)/Time Waits For No One (Jagger, Richards)/
Fool To Cry (Jagger, Richards)/Mannish Boy (London,
McDaniel, Morganfield)/When The Whip Comes
Down (Jagger, Richards)/If I Were A Dancer (Dance
Pt. 2) (Jagger, Richards, Wood)/Crazy Mama (Jagger,
Richards)/Beast Of Burden (Jagger, Richards).

Start Me Up (Jagger, Richard)/**No Use In Crying**
(Jagger, Richard).
Rolling Stones Records RSR 108.
Released: August 17, 1981.

Tattoo You

Rolling Stones Records CUNS 39114.
Released: August 24, 1981.
Produced: The Glimmer Twins.
Start Me Up (Jagger, Richards)/Hang Free (Jagger,
Richards)/Slave (Jagger, Richards)/Little T & A
(Jagger, Richards) /Black Limousine (Jagger, Richards,
Wood)/Neighbours (Jagger, Richards)/Worried About
You (Jagger, Richards)/Tops (Jagger, Richards)/
Heaven (Jagger, Richards)/No Use In Crying (Jagger,
Richards)/Waiting On A Friend (Jagger, Richards).

Waiting On A Friend (Jagger, Richards)/**Little T & A**
(Jagger, Richards).
Rolling Stones Records RSR 109.
Released: November 30, 1981.
Produced: The Glimmer Twins.

Still Life [American concerts 1981]

EMI CUN 39115. Released: June 1, 1982.
Produced: The Glimmer Twins.
Under My Thumb/Let's Spend The Night Together/
Shattered/*Twenty Flight Rock (Fairchild, Cochran)/
**Going To A Go Go (Robinson, Tarplin)/Let Me Go/
Time Is On My Side (Meade, Norman)/Just My
Imagination (Whitfield, Strong)/Start Me Up/
Satisfaction.
All compositions Jagger, Richard except where indicated.

The Lyrics:
Supplement

181
Start Me Up

If you start me up,
If you start me up I'll never stop.

You can start me up, you can start me up I'll
    never stop.
I've been running hot you got me just about to blow
    my top.
You can start me up, you can start me up,
I never stop, never stop, never stop, never stop.
You make a grown man cry, you make a grown
    man cry,
You make a grown man cry, spread out the oil,
    the gasoline.
I walk smooth ride in a mean, mean machine.
Start it up.

You can start me up, kick on the starter, give it all
    you've got.
(You got, you got).
I can't compete with the riders in the other heats.
You rough it up,
If you like it you can slide it up, slide it up,
Slide it up, slide it up.
Don't make a grown man cry, don't make a grown
    man cry,
Don't make a grown man cry, my eyes dilate my lips
    go green
My hands are greasy, she's a mean, mean machine.
Start it up.

Start me up
Ah . . . you've got to, . . . you've got to,
Never, never, never stop.
Start it up,
Ah . . . start it up, never, never, never
You make a grown man cry, you make a grown
    man cry,
You make a grown man cry, ride like the wind at
    double speed
I'll take you places that you've never, never seen.

If you start it up, love the day when we will
    never stop,
Never stop, never, never, never stop.
Tough me up,
Never stop, never stop,
You, you, you make a grown man cry.

182
Hang Fire

In the sweet old country where I come from
Nobody ever works,
Nothing ever gets done.
We Hang Fire.
We Hang Fire.
You know marrying money is a full time job.
I don't need the aggravation,
I'm a lazy slob.
We Hang Fire.
A Hang Fire, Hang Fire, Hang.
Put it on the wire, baby.
Hang Fire, Hang Fire.
Put it on the wire, baby.

We got nothing to eat,
We got nowhere to work.
Nothing to drink
We just lost our shirt.
I'm on the dole
We ain't for hire.
Say what the hell.
Say what the hell.
Hang Fire.
Hang Fire,
Hang Fire, Hang Fire.
Put it on the wire baby.
Hang Fire, Hang Fire, Hang Fire, Hang Fire.
Hang Fire, Hang Fire.
Put it on the wire baby.

Yeh! take a thousand dollars, go and have some fun,
Put it all on at a hundred to one.
Hang Fire.
We Hang Fire.
Put it on the wire baby.

183
Slave

Do it, do it, do it, do it.
Do it, do it, do it, do it.
Don't want to be your slave,
Don't want to be your slave,
Don't want to be your slave,
Don't want to be your slave,
Don't want to be your slave,
Don't want to be your slave.

24 hours a day, hey, why don't you go down to the
    supermarket,
get something to eat, steal something off the shelves,
pass by the liquor store and be back by about quarter
    to 12.

Don't want to be your slave,
Don't want to be your slave,
Don't want to be your slave,
Don't want to be your slave.

Don't want to be your slave,
Don't want to be your slave,
Don't want to be your slave.

Do it, do it, do it, do it, Do it.

184
Tops

Ah aha Hey
Ev'ry-man has the same come on.
I'll make you a star,
I'll take you a million miles from all this
Put you on a pedestal.
Come on, come on, come on.
Have you ever heard those opening lines.
You should leave this small town way behind.
I'll be your partner, show you all the steps,
With me behind you're tasting of the sweet wine
    of success
Cause I'll take you to the top.
Baby (Hey baby.)
I'll take you to the top.
I'll take you to the top.
Baby.
I'll take you to the top.
Step on the ladder toe in the pool.
You're such a natural, you don't need no acting
    school.
Don't need no casting couch, or be a star in bed,
and never, never let success go to your pretty head,
Cause I'll take you to the top.
Baby, I'll swear we're never gonna stop.
Baby, I'll take you to the top.
Baby.
Don't let the world pass you by,
Don't let the world pass you by,
Don't let the world pass you by.
You'd better take your chance now baby,
Or be sorry for the rest of your sweet loving life.
Oh, sugar.
(Hey sugar.)
I'll take you to the top.
I'll take you to the top.
I'll take you to the top.
I'll take you to the top.

185
Neighbours

Neighbours, neighbours, neighbours.
Neighbours
Have I got neighbours.
Have I got neighbours
All day and all night.
Neighbours.
Have I got neighbours.
Ringing my doorbells
All day and all night

Ladies
Have I got crazies,
Screaming young babies,
No peace and no quiet.
TV's. Saxophone playing
Groaning and straining
With the trouble and strife
Is it any wonder,
Is it any wonder,
Is it any wonder.
That we fuss and fight.
But neighbours
Do unto strangers
Do unto neighbours
What you do to yourself, yourself, yourself, yourself
Yourself, yourself.
Neighbours, neighbours, neighbours, neighbours
Neighbours
Do yourself a favour.
Don't you mess with my baby
When I'm working all night.
You know that neighbours
Steal off my table.
Steal off my table.
You're doing all right, all right, all right, all right.
Neighbours
Do unto strangers,
Do unto strangers,
What you do to yourself, yourself, yourself, yourself,
Your–your–your–your–

186
Little T&A

She's my little rock and roll, ah, ah, ah.
Oh, oh, she's my little rock and roll baby.

The heat's raiding tracks are fading.
Joint's rocking, could be any time at all,
But the bitch keeps bitching, the
Snitcher keeps snitching.
Dropping names and telephone numbers and all.
Ah.

She's my little rock and roll, ah, ah, ah, ah.
Oh, oh, she's my little rock and roll baby.

Scars healing, the dealer's squealing.
The pool's in but the patio ain't dry.
Well the sense is sensing that the juice keeps pumping
    and I know why.

She's my little rock and roll.
Ah. Ah.
My tits and ass with soul baby.
She's my little rock and roll. Ah.
Oh, oh. She's my little rock and roll. Ha!
You got to shock them, show them,
She's my little rock and roll.
Yeah.
Shock, shock, shock, my, my
Well the sense is sensing that the juice keeps pumping
    and I know why.
But the bitch keeps bitching, the
Snitcher keeps snitching.
Dropping names and telephone numbers and all.
She's my little rock and roll.
Ah. Ah.
My tits and ass with soul baby.
She's my little rock and roll. Ah.
Got to shock them, show them.
She's my little rock and roll
Ah Ha She got a feeling to know, baby
She's my little rock and roll
Hey the little bitch got soul.

187

Black Limousine

We used to ride baby
Ride around in limousines,
We looked so fine baby.
You in white and me in green
Drinking and dancing,
All inside and crazy dream.
Well now look at your face now baby and look at you
And look at me.
I get so scared
Just to see you on the street,
They're living dead
You're all the same, you never speak
You're wrecked out now,
Washed up high up on the beach.
Well now look at your face now baby and look at you
And look at me.
We used to shine (Shine, shine, shine)
Say, what a pair, say what a team.
We used to ride (Ride, ride, ride)
Ride in a long black limousine
Those dreams are gone baby
They're locked away and never seen.
Well now look at your face now baby and look at you
And look at me.

188

Heaven

Hmm–Hmm–Hmm–Hmm
Smell of your body, my senses, my senses be praised.
Smell of your body, my senses, my senses be praised.
Ooh, Yeah, Mm, Yeah,
Kissing and running, kissing and running away,
Kissing and running, kissing and running away.
Mm Senses be praised,
Mm Senses be praised.
Mm You're saving grace
Mm Saving saving grace;
Nothing will harm you, nothing will stand in your
    your way.
Mm Nothing will stop you and nothing will stand in
    your way, your way.

No-one will harm you, no-one will stand in your way.
No-one will bar you, nothing will stand in the way.
Nothing, there's nothing
No-no-no-no-no-no-no-no-no-no-no-no-no-thing.
Hey yah yah yah yah yah yah.
Hey yah yah yah yah yah yah yah yah yah yah.

ng On A Friend

Watching girls go passing by it ain't the latest thing
I'm just standing in a door-way
I'm just trying to make some sense.
Out of these girls passing by,
The tales they tell of men.
I'm not waiting on a lady,
I'm just waiting on a friend.
Mm

A smile relieves a heart that grieves,
Remember what I said.
I'm not waiting on a lady,
I'm just waiting on a friend.

Just waiting on a friend.
I'm just waiting on a friend,
I'm just waiting on a friend,
Just waiting on a friend.

Don't need a whore, don't need no booze,
Don't need a virgin priest.
But I need some-one I can cry to.
I need some-one to protect.

Ooh, making love and breaking hearts,
It is a game for youth.
But I'm not waiting on a lady.
I'm just waiting on a friend.

I'm just waiting on a friend,
Just waiting on a friend.
I'm just waiting on a friend,
I'm just waiting on a friend,
Just waiting on a friend.

Worried About You

Sometimes I wonder why you do these things to me,
Sometimes I worry girl, that you ain't in love with me,
Sometimes I stay out late – yeah – I'm having fun.
Yes I guess you know by now that you ain't the
    only one.
Yeah and baby ooh, sweet things that you
    promised me,
Seemed to go up in smoke, yeah vanish like a dream.
Baby, I wonder why yeah, you do these things to me.
Cause I'm worried, yeah, I just can't seem to find
    my way
Baby

Ooh, the nights I spend just waiting on the sun,
Just like your burned out cigarette you threw me and
    my love.
(Why d'you do that baby?)
I wonder why, why – you do these things to me.
Babe, Oh I'm worried

Lord I'll find out anyway, sure gonna find myself a
    girl someday
Till then I'll worry, yeah,
I just can't seem to find my way.

Yeah, I'm a hard working man
When did I ever do you wrong,
Yeah I get all my money baby (Yeah Yeah)
Bring it, bring it on home.
(Now tell the truth, yeah)
The sweet things. (The sweet things)
Now that you promised me.
Well I'm worried and I just can't seem to find
    my way.

Baby, Ah, Ah,
I'm worried 'bout you, yeah,
I'm worried about you
Yeah, I'm worried Lord
I'll find out any-way.
Sure as hell I'm gonna find
A girl someday,
Oh, I'm worried Lord,
I just can't seem to find my way.

191
No Use In Crying

Ain't no use in crying,
Stay away from me.
Ain't no use in crying,
Stay away from me.
Ain't no use in crying,
Stay away from me.

Standing in the kitchen
Looking 'way out across the fields.
You see a face in the window.
It's not real
It's not real,
Ain't no use in crying.
Stay away from me, Stay away,
Ain't no use, Ain't no use.
Ain't no use. Ain't no use
Ain't no use,
Stay away from me.
Stay away, Ain't no use in crying.
Stay away from me.
Stay away.
Standing at the station
And gazing down the track.
There ain't no train coming baby.
I ain't never, never coming back.
Standing at the balcony.
Looking way out towards the sea,
If you see your ship come a sailing,
It's not me.
It's not me, It's not me It's not me,
It's not me, It's not me.
Ain't no use, Ain't no use.
Stay away, Ain't no use in crying.
Stay away stay away from me.
Ain't no use in crying.
Stay away from me.

192
Everything Is Turning
To Gold

I don't care if your love grows cold
Found love in someone else's home.
Don't like standin' in the snow.

Ev'rything's turning to gold.
Ev'rything's turnin' to gold.
Ev'rything's turnin' to gold.

2nd verse
You used to know me long ago;
Was so lost and way down low.
Now that the love juice starts to flow,
Now that the love juice starts to flow,
Ev'rything's turning to gold,
Ev'rything's turning to gold.

Ev-'ry-thing's turn - in', (ev-'ry-thing is turn - in'.)

Ev-'ry-thing's turn - in', (turn - in', turn - in',)

Ev-'rything's turn - in', (ev-'ry-thing is turn-in'
   to gold.)

3rd verse
I'm tired, I'm tired of doing what I'm told.
Things are moving way too slow.
I got no problems; I got no problems, child.
It ain't my business; it ain't my business, ain't
   my style.
Now that the love juice starts to flow,
Now that the love juice starts to flow.

If I Were A Dancer
(Dance Part 2)

Verse 1
I stand accused of talking, but I feel that we are
   falling in the same old groove.
The radio is playing, spitting out the same old news.
It's time to get up, and out; out into something new.
Time to get up, and out, out into something new.

1,2,4.
If I was a woman, I would want a new man ev'ry night.

Verses 2, 3, 5
Everybody wants somebody's fantasy;
Everybody wants somebody's crazy dreams.

Bridge 3
If I was a politician,
I'd make sure I was a fancy dancer.

Verse 4
The poor man eyes the rich man,
Who denigrates his poverty.
The rich man eyes the poor man,
And envies his simplicity.

Bridge
5. If I was a movie star, five million dollars would
   be my price.
6. If I was a trucker, I'd drive seven days and
   seven lonely nights.
7. If I was a drummer, I'd never miss a beat.
8. If I was a dancer, y' all would never see my feet.
9. If I was a hooker, a thousand dollars would be
   my price all right.
10. If I was a candidate for President, I'd make
    sure I had a steady wife.
11. If I was a millionaire, I'd spend it all in one
    crazy night.

The Music: Supplement

181

Start Me Up

You can start me up,
Kick on the starter, give it all you've got.
(You got, you got).
I can't compete with the riders in the other heats.
You rough it up,
If you like it you can slide it up,
Slide it up, slide it up, slide it up.
Don't make a grown man cry,
Don't make a grown man cry,
Don't make a grown man cry,
My eyes dilate, my lips go green
My hands are greasy, she's a mean, mean machine.
Start it up.

Start me up, Ah
You've got to, you've got to, you've got to, never, never, never stop.
Start it up, Ah, start it up,
Never, never, never,
You make a grown man cry,
You make a grown man cry,
You make a grown man cry,
Ride like the wind at double speed,
I'll take you places that you've never, never seen.
(To Coda)

182
Hang Fire

You know mar-ry-ing mon-ey is a

Fast rock

Do do do do do do do do

full time job. I don't need the ag-gra-va-tion, I'm a

Do do do do do do do do

laz-y slob. We Hang Fire.   A' Hang

do do do. In the
           Yeh!

Fire, Hang Fire, Hang., Put it on the wire, ba-by

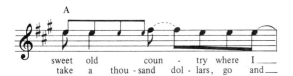

sweet old coun-try where I
take a thou-sand dol-lars, go and

Hang Fire, Hang Fire.

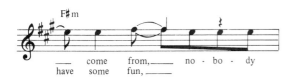

come from, no-bo-dy
have some fun,

Put it on the wire, ba-by   Fire.)

ev — er works, Noth-ing
Put it all on at a

Hang.

ev er gets done, We Hang
hun-dred to one, Hang

We got Noth-ing to eat, We got

To Coda ⊕

Fire. We Hang Fire.
Fire. We Hang Fire.

no-where to work. Noth-ing to drink. We

just lost our shirt. I'm on the dole.

We ain't for hire.— Say what the hell—

Say what the hell. Hang Fire.———— Hang Fire,—

— Hang Fire, Hang Fire. Put it on the wire— ba-by.

Hang Fire, Hang Fire, Hang Fire,——

— Hang Fire. Hang Fire, Hang Fire.

D.C. al Coda

Put it on the wire—— ba-by.

⊕ *CODA*

Put it on the wire— ba-by. Do do do do

Do do do do Do do do do

do do do do. do do do do.

183
Slave

Slow beat

Do it, do it, do it, do it,

do it. Do it, do it, do it, do it,—

(Both times)

— Don't want to be your

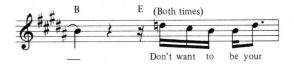

slave,— Don't want to be your

184

Tops

Oh, su-gar. (Hey

su-gar.) I'll take you to the top. ___

Repeat ad lib. to Fade

I'll take you to the top. ___

I'll take you to the top. Baby.
(Hey Baby.)
I'll take you to the top.
I'll take you to the top. Baby.
I'll take you to the top.
Step on the ladder, toe in the pool.
You're such a natural, you don't need no acting school.
Don't need no casting couch, or be a star in bed,
And never never let success go
To your pretty head, 'cause I

I'll take you to the top. Baby,
ad lib. I'll swear we're never gonna stop. Baby,
I'll take you to the top. Baby.

(To Coda)

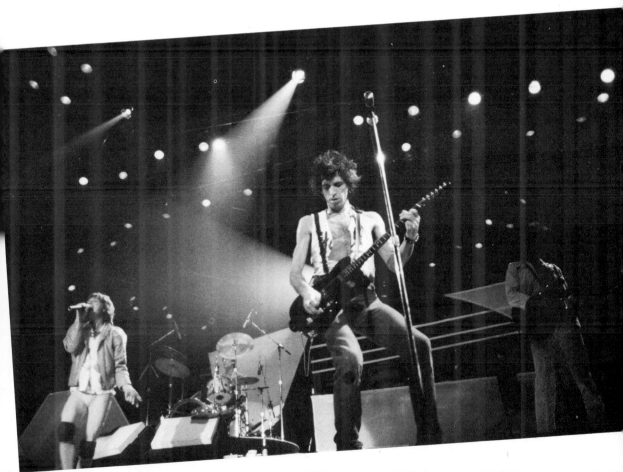

185
Neighbours

self, your - self, your - self, your - self.

D.%. and begin fade at *

Neigh - bours, neigh - bours, neigh-bours, neigh-bours.

Neighbours, Do yourself a favour.
Don't you mess with my baby
When I'm working all night.
You know that neighbours,
Steal off my table.
Steal off my table.
You're doing all right, all right, all right, all right.

Neighbours do unto strangers,
Do unto strangers
What you do to yourself,
Yourself, yourself, yourself, your- your- your- *(etc. ad lib.)*

Little T&A

Moderate rock

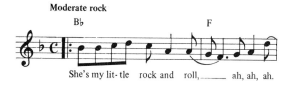

She's my lit-tle rock and roll,＿ ah, ah, ah.

Oh, oh,＿

she's my lit-tle rock and roll＿ ba - by.＿

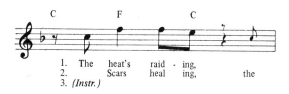

1. The heat's raid - ing,
2. Scars heal ing, the
3. *(Instr.)*

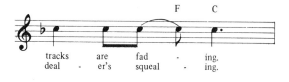

tracks are fad - ing.
deal - er's squeal - ing.

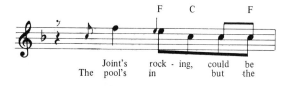

Joint's rock - ing, could be
The pool's in but the

an - y time＿ at all,＿ But the
pat - i - o＿ ain't dry.＿

bitch keeps bitch - ing, the
(2) Well the

Snitch - er keeps snitch - ing.
sense is sens - ing that the

Drop - ping names＿ and tel - e - phone num -
juice keeps pump - ing and I

bers and all.＿ Ah.＿ (know why.)＿
＿ bers and all.

She's my lit - tle rock and roll.＿ Ah, ah.

My tits and ass with soul＿ ba - by.

To Coda ⊕

She's my lit - tle rock and roll.＿ Ah.＿

Oh, ＿ oh.

She's my lit -tle rock and roll,＿ Ha!

187

Black Limousine

You got to shock them, show them,

She's my lit-tle rock and roll._____ Yeah.

Shock,   shock,

shock,   my,_ my_____ (2) Well the

sense is sens-ing that the juice keeps pump-ing and I

—D.%. al Coda

know why   But the

⊕CODA

Got to shock them, show_ them.

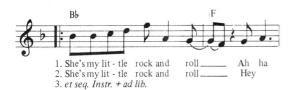

1. She's my lit-tle rock and roll_____ Ah ha
2. She's my lit-tle rock and roll_____ Hey
3. et seq. Instr. + ad lib.

Repeat ad lib. to Fade

She got a feel-ing to   know,_ ba-by
the lit-tle bitch got   soul._

Swing

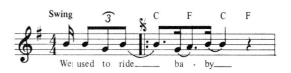

We used to ride_____ ba - by_

Ride a-round_ in lim-ou-sines,

We looked so fine_

ba - by._

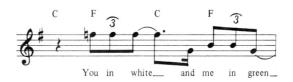

You in white_ and me in green_

Drink-ing and danc-

- ing. _

All   in-side_ and cra-zy dream._

Well_ now look at your face now ba-by

and look at you and look at me.

I get so scared   Instrumental

We used to shine

I get so scared baby
just to see you on the street,
They're living dead
You're all the same, you never speak.
You're wrecked out now,
Washed up high up on the beach.

We used to shine (Shine, shine, shine.)
Say, what a pair, say, what a team.
We used to ride (Ride, ride, ride.)
Ride in a long black limousine.
Those dreams are gone baby
They're locked away and never seen.

188

Heaven

Medium slow beat

Hmm _____ Hmm _____

_____   Smell of your bo-dy, my

sen-ses, my sen-ses be praised._____

Smell of your bo-dy, my

sen-ses, my sen-ses be praised._____

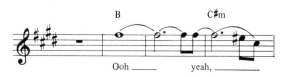

Ooh _____ yeah, _____

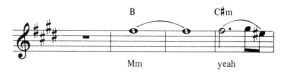

Mm   yeah

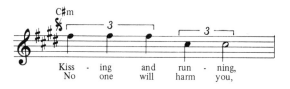

Kiss - ing   and   run - ning,
No   one   will   harm   you,

No - no - no - no - no - no no - no - no - no - no - no - no - no - thing, __

Hey yah yah yah yah yah yah.

Hey yah yah yah

yah yah yah yah yah yah yah.

189
Waiting On A Friend

D.S. (with repeat)
to fade on instrumental

A smile relieves a heart that grieves,
Remember what I said.
I'm not waiting on a lady,
I'm just waiting on a friend.

Don't need a whore, don't need no booze,
Don't need a virgin priest.
But I need someone I can cry to,
I need someone to protect.

Ooh, making love and breaking hearts,
It is a game for youth.
But I'm not waiting on a lady,
I'm just waiting on a friend.

190

Worried About You

191
No Use In Crying

Nights I spend just waiting on the sun,
Just like your burned out cigarette.
You threw me and my love.
(Why d'you do that baby?)
I wonder why,
Why you do these things to me.
Babe. Oh I'm worried *(etc.)*

Yeah, I'm a hard working man
When did I ever do you wrong,
Yeah I get all my money baby
(Yeah, yeah.)
Bring it, bring it on home.
(Now tell the truth, yeah.)
The sweet things. (The sweet things.)
Now that you promised me.
Well I'm worried *(etc.)*

Everything Is Turning To Gold

Moderately fast, with a strong beat

1. Don't care if your love grows cold
2 & 3.—see additional lyric.

found love in some-one el - se's home.

Don't like stand-in' in the snow.

Ev-'ry-thing's turn - in' to gold.

Ev-'ry-thing's turn - in' to gold.

Ev-'ry - thing's turn - in' to gold.

1 Ev-'ry - thing's turn - in' to gold.

Ev-'ry - thing's turn - in' to gold.

2 Ev-'ry-thing's turn - in', (ev-'ry-thing is turn-in'.)

Ev-'ry-thing's turn - in', (turn - in', turn - 'in',)

Ev-'ry-thing's turn - in', (ev-'ry-thing is turn-in' to gold.)

play 3 times

D.%. al Coda

3. I'm

CODA

Now that the love juice starts to flow,

ev-'ry-thing's turn-in' to gold.

Ev-'ry-thing's turn - in'.

play 3 times

Ev-'ry-thing's turn - in', (ev-'ry-thing is turn-in')

Repeat and fade

Ev-'ry-thing's turn - in', (turn - in', turn - in'.)

2nd verse
You used to know me long ago;
Was so lost and way down low.
Now that the love juice starts to flow,
Now that the love juice starts to flow,
Ev'rything's turning to gold,
Ev'rything's turning to gold.

3rd verse
I'm tired, I'm tired of doing what I'm told.
Things are moving way too slow.
I got no problems; I got no problems, child.
It ain't my business; it ain't my business, ain't my style.
Now that the love juice starts to flow,
Now that the love juice starts to flow,

(to Coda)

193

If I Were A Dancer
(Dance Part 2)

Verses 2, 3, 5
Everybody wants somebody's fantasy:
Everybody wants somebody's crazy dreams.

Bridge 3.
If I was a politician,
I'd make sure I was a fancy dancer.

Verse 4:
The poor man eyes the rich man,
Who denigrates his poverty.
The rich man eyes the poor man,
And envies his simplicity.

Bridge:
5. If I was a movie star, five million dollars would be my price.
6. If I was a trucker, I'd drive seven days and seven lonely nights.
7. If I was a drummer, I'd never miss a beat
8. If I was a dancer, y' all would never see my feet.
9. If I was a hooker, a thousand dollars would be my price all right.
10. If I was a candidate for President, I'd make sure I had a steady wife.
11. If I was a millionaire, I'd spend it all in one crazy night.